DYNAMICS
of VIOLENCE

Edited By:

Jan Fawcett, MD

Library of Congress Catalog Card Number: 79-169740

Price: 1-10 copies--U.S., Poss., Canada & Mexico: $3.95 each.
11 or more copies--U.S., Poss., Canada & Mexico: $2.95 each.
Med. students, Hosp. interns & residents in U.S., Poss.,
    Canada & Mexico: $1.95 each.

CONTENTS

INTRODUCTION

A seven-year-old boy murders his brother with a shotgun. A man with a fear of being touched goes berserk, stabbing seven people in four days. Volunteers in a psychological experiment willingly subject innocent "victims" to supposedly painful electric shocks. A war no one can win drags on for years, taking the lives of thousands of soldiers.

What all these events have in common is the presence of aggression as a motivating factor to an act of violence. Not the ordinary form of aggression in most of us—the instinctive drive for self-assertion that makes us discover continents, build cities and fly to the moon—but aggression distorted pathologically into violence, a destructive, sometimes deadly mutation of a normally constructive human trait.

The results of violent aggression, such as the incidents listed above—all true —are well-known and widely discussed, but its causes are mystifying and unclear. As a topic of scientific interest, violent aggression has received surprisingly little study until very recently, when a combination of factors made us all more aware of violence than we have ever been before.

This is an age in which millions can witness, through television, the murder of Lee Harvey Oswald, the Viet Nam War, or the streetfighting between police and college students. Violence surrounds our daily lives; we read about it in newspapers, we see it on television, occasionally witness it in person, and when we want to escape the pressure of modern life, we find violence in our books and movies, and even in the toys our children play with. Its forms are amazingly varied: arguments, fistfights, stabbings, shootings, rapes, arson, bombings, riots, and international wars. Perhaps there is no more bloodshed and violence than in the past, but never has it been with us so constantly. It has even become a political issue, under the disguise of "crime in the streets."

Science and technology have provided us with engines of violence from the automobile to the atomic bomb and as yet unnamed weapons of mass destruction. But little has yet been offered which might avert the present capacity for

1

total self-destruction afforded by these advances. Little knowledge has been contributed to the dynamics of mass capacity for brutality and murder which have become evident through the bloodstains of history. Now that we have the means for destruction of life "perfected" beyond previous imagination, we must turn the creative power of science against the prose of violence.

Choosing to study a problem so immense and complicated, where do you begin? You can start by simply theorizing about the subject, drawing general lines of thought and points of view for further study, to be discussed—and amplified—by others and their comments reported; you can observe it as it occurs in mental hospitals, prisons, clinics, and psychiatrists' offices, recording and analyzing each individual case; or you can construct controlled experiments that painstakingly build a scientific foundation for understanding. Thanks to the size and diversity of our medical and scientific community, every approach possible is now being taken.

The articles selected for this book are the outgrowth of a midwest regional meeting of The American Psychiatric Association in cooperation with the American Medical Association, Lester H. Rudy, M.D., general chairman. They represent all three approaches to the nature, causes, dynamics, and dimensions of violence: theoretical discussions, clinical observations and research conclusions. They represent the best work on the subject in nearly every field of medicine and psychology; consequently the nature of the articles runs a spectrum from the very general to the very specific.

No single article supplies all the answers; in fact, the entire collection does not supply all the answers—or even all the questions. But as in all scientific study, the book and the articles in it are meant to provide a greater understanding for coping with this problem on a clinical basis as well as a stepping-stone for greater research.

SECTION 1

GENERAL PERSPECTIVES

This first section contains papers of a theoretical and general nature. Dr. Lawrence Kolb's overview outlines the major dimensions for a consideration of violence and aggression, from biological factors through individual psychology to ethology and sociological factors. We learn that there are a number of important foci about which further knowledge must be developed, and which must be seen in relation to each other if we are to understand the phenomenon of violence at both the individual and group level.

Historical and social dimensions are added by Dr. John Spiegel's penetrating analysis of cycles of violence in our national history. The picture becomes more imposing, real and awesome as Dr. Jerome Frank considers psychological factors of relevance to international conflict and war. We are offered a grim reminder we so often try to deny that our very existence is at stake. Perhaps Dr. Frank's paper will stimulate some leaders to ask what mental health professionals might contribute to the prevention of war.

Dr. Seymour Halleck's critique of our penal system refocuses our attention on the shortcomings of our own institutions of justice in dealing with violent and criminal behavior; and Dr. Roy R. Grinker, Sr., concludes the section with remarks in response to the program of the Midwest Conference.

The papers in this section, taken together, encompass many of the major issues raised by violent and aggressive behavior in our world society. They offer positive suggestions, based on available observations of both group and individual behavior, for the control of violence in an increasingly complex social and technological environment.

VIOLENCE AND AGGRESSION
An Overview

Lawrence C. Kolb, M.D.

An optimistic and persuasive picture of violence is painted by Lorenz—the control of aggression through the evolutionary development of patterns of behavior within species.[1] This colorful picture of aggression as a ritualized give-and-take based on territorial behavior leaves out the savagery and naked violence exemplified even in the animal kingdom by works such as *Shark Attack* by Coppleson.[2] Among men there may be a ritualized give-and-take, a form taken by aggressive behavior which has a certain survival value for our species, but this is only one aspect of human violence. It is clear that we cannot rest on optimistic assumptions of a biological purpose in facing human violence, especially in light of our recent history.

The history of mankind records that at best only 10 generations in the era of recorded history have avoided war—and war as an expression of violence across the world appears to erupt at the rate of 2½ wars per year.[3] We are fearfully preoccupied with the matter of overt and violent aggression among our own species. As Americans, we have been exposed in recent times to a series of shocking multiple murders: the assassinations of Medgar Evers, Malcolm X, John F. Kennedy, George Lincoln Rockwell, Martin Luther King, Jr. and Robert F. Kennedy, men of differing skin colors and political and religious affinities. There have been massive non-violent protests, violent and destructive riots in our cities, aggressive and violent eruptions on university and college campuses.

Of the violent group protests, some seemed spontaneously triggered, while others followed consciously contrived provocation. Each day countless other aggressive and violent acts take place but go unnoticed. We are engaged in a war in Vietnam. At the same time we casually kill more and maim many more

---

Dr. Kolb is director of the New York State Psychiatric Institute and professor and chairman of the Columbia University College of Physicians and Surgeons, New York, New York.

each year with our modern juggernaut of transportation, the automobile, than we lose in the Vietnam conflict.

But is there actually more violence in our society now than before?[4] In 1786 there was the Shays farmers' rebellion. During the Civil War, the draft riots in New York City ended with 900 dead and 10,000 seriously injured. The assassinations of early presidents; the long history of successive riots directed against Catholics, Irish, Chinese and, more recently, against Mexican immigrants; the many labor strikes, as well as the anti-Negro riots commencing in the early 1920's, and the history of riots in other nations continues to be impressive but generally forgotten or ignored.

The optimistic viewpoint is that since 1946, over a span of 20 years, the people of the world have avoided a holocaust of violence which could exceed in destructiveness for mankind in a few moments the worst that he has inflicted upon himself, even at the height of World War II.

Is there in fact an increase in aggressiveness and violence in our society or in mankind in general? Currently, there are no means of measuring violence effectively. But one fact is certain! Since the beginning of this decade, there has been a mounting crescendo of communications reporting individual and collective acts of aggression and violence. The number of scientific and popular articles and books, the radio reports and the rapidly expanding representation of violence on television reach the public in a magnitude beyond comprehension.

Particularly in this country, the television audience has been exposed to an uninterrupted series of visual portrayals of violence. Each watcher has available a ready means of learning violence, of releasing aggressive fantasies and perhaps gratifying violent wishes.[5] It is also certain that our social, political, economic and scientific leaders have yet to direct sufficient attention through research to determining the potential effect of television and other communications media on the release of violence in society.

The social, biological and psychological sciences[3, 6, 7, 8, 9, 10, 11, 12] have given us much information on the aggressive drive and its expression in acts of violence. That knowledge, applied perhaps only fitfully and doubtfully by scientific bodies, has not deterred wide-scale violence. What is taking place in this country today raises questions about the communication of that knowledge to the appropriate sources of political power and its potential for guidelines for political strategy. But have we established theories with predictability that may alleviate violence as an expression of aggression? Many groups need to come to grips with these questions in order to determine and communicate what is known and what may be done. We need to do so to stimulate research in areas where our knowledge is incomplete.

In a sense, we are interested not primarily in aggression and its expression in violence. The focus is much narrower. Our interest and dedication are in the *control* of violence. Comparative psychologists, ethologists and zoologists have collected enough data to show that aggression, even if defined in the very narrow sense of initiating attack,[13] is a universal form of behavior in all classes of vertebrates and arthropods. The studies of the comparative ethologists show that fighting *per se* in the animal kingdom is common, useful and apparently adaptive.[1, 13] As a behavior, it is concerned with survival of a species.

These biological observations have important implications in the study of control mechanisms and have bearing, too, on certain hypotheses held by some psychoanalysts. The animal studies demonstrate that both the external and internal physical environment are influential in modulating impulsiveness. Thus, exposure to low temperatures early in life increases impulsiveness and exposure to high temperatures early in life reduces aggressiveness in animals. Hunger, territorial restriction, and the increase in male sex hormone increase fighting in various vertebrates. Many ethologists and neurophysiologists conceptualize their studies on aggression under the wider abstraction of agonistic behavior. Expression of aggression and reactions to aggression—rage and fight, immobilization, flight—are the agonistic responses designed to protect each species from attack and also to facilitate feeding and sexual activities.

Over the years psychiatrists have investigated many perpetrators of the most dramatic peacetime form of violence—murder. Individual murderers, mass murderers, presidential assassins, male and female murderers all have claimed our attention. Also subject to investigation have been contributing biological and social factors, personality types, and personality development and its dynamics.

The political assassins have been almost all psychopathic with long and grim experiences of emotional deprivation and abnormal rearing.[14] These include Lee Harvey Oswald,[15] his killer, Ruby, and finally Sirhan Sirhan. But before the recent political assassinations, we were horrified by a series of mass murders, as in the Whitman case in Austin, Texas. That case, and the testimony given before the courts pertaining to alleged abnormality in the electroencephalogram of Jack Ruby, touched off a restudy of the possible relationship of biological factors—that is, factors impairing brain development and function which might contribute to failure in the control of emergent violence.

Studies of convicted murderers in this country and abroad have shown that, where there seems to be normal brain functioning, a higher percentage of those convicted of unmotivated murders have abnormal EEG's than those who killed in self-defense.[16] Alcohol, that widely used solvent of brain functioning, particularly the superego expressions of functioning, has been imbibed in excessive quantities by many who murder. The evidence piles up that the powerful hallucinogens also destroy impulse control; some persons have murdered while under their influence.

We know too that many children with brain disease have impaired capacity to absorb and learn the mores of society from their parents. If they do learn, their impulse control often is less than that of their healthier peers. Their control of drives, including their aggressive drive, is subject to rapid dissolution under extraordinary conditions of anxiety or when brain functioning is temporarily further impaired. Clinicians for centuries have been aware of personality changes with violent aggressiveness which sometimes follow head injuries that occur in some persons with convulsive disorders, and which not infrequently erupt in some individuals after they imbibe small amounts of alcohol.[14]

The violent individual deserves careful neurological study as well as psychiatric examination. This is not to say that the "dyscontrol syndrome," as it has been designated, is due solely to impairment of brain functioning, but rather that socially acceptable and learned control of aggression is more likely to fail, and release of primitive and destructive action occurs more readily, in those with some impairment of brain function.

The study of murderers elicits such massive evidence of emotional deprivation in early life, however, that we cannot rest our assumptions about violence in man on impairment of brain function alone. The brain records experiences, and effective patterns of behavioral response may be established to cope with the varying stimuli that characterize social existence.

Every physician should become acquainted with Wertham's study of Irwin, the multiple murderer of New York City,[17] as well as with the study of Germany's famous Wagner case of 1913. Wagner killed nine persons and wounded 12 more after living a seemingly passive life for years as a village school teacher. But he harbored a paranoid grudge based on latent homosexual fear which went unrecognized until his murderous carnage.[18] Irwin's illness was known beforehand; but how does one detect the potential for violence in a patient throughout succeeding years of life so that it may be predicted and controlled?

Perhaps because inappropriate aggressiveness impresses us more dramatically, clinical and laboratory studies of the physiological processes related to the expression of rage preceded studies of other forms of behavior. As early as 1892, Goltz[19] reported on the behavior of a decorticated dog, which displayed strong actions of growling, barking and biting on slight stimulation. These actions are expressive of rage.

Cannon coined the term "sham rage" after he observed lashing of the tail, arching of the back, display of claws, biting, and panting respiration—behavior which showed the components of rage and attack in acutely decorticated cats.[14]

A long series of arousal experiments by Bard, Mountcastle and others,[20] demonstrated that "savage" behavior in cats followed precise lesions in the ventromedial nucleus of the hypothalamus.

It is now known that the removal of the neocortex alone, leaving the old brain rhinencephalic structures intact, leads to the behavioral expression of placidity—the obverse of rage. Rage reactions emerge spontaneously when both new and old cortices are removed, or when the amygdala and pyriform cortex are resected, but not after damage to the hippocampus. The neocortex then appears to have both a facilitory and an inhibitory influence on aggressive behaviors characterized by rage. In addition it influences the direction and timing of such behaviors. The inhibitory influence is dependent upon the cingulate gyrus and transmitted through the amygdala to influence the ventro-medial hypothalamic nuclei.

The introduction of prefrontal lobotomy made possible more precise studies of the relationship of functions of the brain to the control of emotions. As a result of many observations of psychiatrically ill persons treated by prefrontal lobotomy, the clinical indications for the procedure were narrowed to certain symptoms which represent the expression of rage or related aggressive states: assaultive and destructive behavior, suicidal acts, chronic irascibility, agitation, undue anxiety, impulsivity and over-activity.

Other behavioral symptoms suppressed by lobotomy are depression, hypochondriasis, chronic pain and refusal to eat. These symptoms are interpreted in the clinic as symbolic of inhibition of rage or hostility. Lobotomy offers little in terms of the social adaptation of the psychotic patient who shows apathy and indifference. It has been found as well that prefrontal cortical resections made in a posterior plane, which presumably damaged the amygdala, induced apathy or placidity that mitigated against the social recovery of the patient.[14]

The weakness of pharmacologic research using animals as subjects rests upon the inability to examine the effectiveness of certain agents in prevention of aggressive and violent behavior.[21] Work with animals examines change in aggressivity after it has been induced experimentally. Lack of handling early in life, injection of male sex hormone, painful stimulation, bilateral lesions in the limbic system, (olfactory bulbs, lateral olfactory tracts and prepyriform cortex), administrations of LSD, amphetamines, adrenochrome, L-dopa, 5 HTP, and chlorodimethylpromide are means of increasing aggressivity in animals. There are no studies of animals in the free state under varying environmental stresses. For these we must turn to the human species.

The evidence from both clinic and hospital makes it clear that the phenothiazines inhibit aggressive behaviors and their accompanying effects in man. However, in the clinic it appears that the most significant decrease in social aggression takes place only among chlorpromazine-treated patients who live in low tension and low conflict homes.[22] Such drug treatment is less likely to be effective if the individual to whom it is administered is dissonant with family interactional patterns and more likely if he is consonant with them.

Pharmacology has made a significant contribution to our ability to control violence. Between the tranquilizers and the new analogues of the nerve gases (notably chemical mace) which paralyze the neuromuscular system we have means of quickly terminating outbreaks of individual or collective aggression. So far as we know these agents act without permanently harming the individual. Undoubtedly, scientists will attempt to develop newer agents which will more clearly suppress the aggressive arousal.

Biologic, physiologic and pharmacologic evidence demonstrates the existence of an aggressive potential within each vertebrate organism. The evidence is overwhelming and cannot be denied. Its existence supports the assumption that aggressive behavior is an important adaptive response which facilitates many activities concerned with both self-preservation and preservation of the species. But to understand the control of aggression, we must examine this innate drive in its complex relationship to other drives—those concerned with mating and rearing of young and those from which the human emotions of love, tenderness, and compassion are generated.

Some wish for a world in which there is a complete suppression or abolition of the aggressive drive. As clinicians we know what the dire consequences would be. Our state institutions are filled largely with those who suffer the paralyzing inhibition of aggression—the vast number of apathetic and withdrawn schizophrenics and the elderly whose brain damage has impaired their energetic capacity.

To be sure, some of our colleagues believe that schizophrenia is a way of life rather than a disease.[23] For most psychiatrists there are more adaptive and more gratifying ways of living. The successful therapy of the neuroses depends largely on the removal of inhibitions against healthy aggressiveness and sexuality.

Our department of mental health is often asked how much former hospitalized patients contribute to violence when returned to the community. The majority of studies made in the past have found that criminal action, including violence, was less in the group of discharged patients than in the general population. Rappaport[24] in the most recent report found differences in types of violence but not in frequency.

The original challenge to psychiatry in its role as protector of the community was made before the introduction of the open door hospital policy and the widespread use of tranquilizers. This question is one to which our biometric and epidemiologic associates should repeatedly return. In our therapeutic enthusiasm we must not forget that our hospital systems were erected to provide both asylum for the ill and protection for society. We should not forget that hospitals are one of the institutions used by society to bring about social homeostasis. The judgments that must be made relative to release of patients require the use of skilled and experienced professionals.

When it comes to successful control of aggressivity expressed as violence in patient populations, in spite of our recent successes through administration of the phenothiazines, the challenge to psychiatry remains enormous, particularly in the personality disorders and the psychopathies. These patients find their way more often to the courts and correctional institutions than to our private offices, clinics and hospitals.

Man, whose brain can store and integrate information from experience and who is capable of the most complex intellectual feats, has the potential to evolve a world-wide code of social behavior which can control destructive acting out.

Man's control of violence depends upon the evolution of his *superego* or *conscience*, individually and collectively. The conscience depends upon a particular functional organization of his brain, a series of repetitive experiences within the family or its surrogate, and their support by a related community.

As Brosin[25] recently reminded us, Darwin termed the historical emergence of conscience as man's greatest achievement. It had its beginnings in the early Nile valley agricultural societies some 4,000 to 5,000 years ago. Through the use of religion, man has come to control many of the consequences of frustration in social life; his unmet desires, hopes, fears and anxieties. He erected an elaborate system of psychological adaptations which made his expressions of aggression so complex that it was necessary to find a Freud to unravel their meanings.

The initial efforts to control aggressive and sexual behavior were the responsibility of the family, supported later by the ritual of the culture. These controls were held and still are held largely by "in groups" in each culture, although easily abrogated in times of collective conflict, such as war. Nonviolent or consciously contrived group threats of violence, in which words or gestures symbolize the aggressive potential have been highly successful in bringing social change in countries where the Judeo-Christian ethic is strong.

History shows, however, that authoritarian rulers, such as Genghis Khan, are not deterred by a mass conscience from violently achieving their goals of conquest or subjugation. That many may be capable of a collective conscience seems possible now, although, in the United Nations today, only lip service is given to shame the aggressions of major nations against their smaller neighbors.

Psychiatry and psychoanalysis[7, 26, 27, 28, 29] have made major contributions to the understanding of violence particularly in relation to its expression by the individual. Knowledge of individual psychologic processes contributes to the understanding of forms of socially condoned violence, and violent interactions between the individual and groups.

Through psychoanalytic hypotheses and the methods stimulated by psychoanalysis to study life experiences as the dynamic forces through which personality evolves, we have come to recognize the importance of early nurturing as a means to control and direct the aggressive drive.

At first, Freud referred to aggression as a component of the sexual impulse. In 1917, he hypothesized that aggression was aroused when pleasure seeking or avoidance of pain was blocked—that is, aggression was the result of frustration. Only later, as a result of the study of depression, did he refer to aggression as an independent and primary drive with a destructive component which he called the death instinct. It was Freud's hypotheses[26] that the aggressive impulse in man is aroused by frustration. This hypothesis inspired Dollard and his co-workers[30] to elaborate a series of subsidiary hypotheses for which they found support in accounts of a variety of human actions. These hypotheses are pertinent to our current thinking about the management of violence. Therefore, allow me to repeat them:

1. Aggression is regulated by the ingroup.
2. Aggression is expressed against those who are competitors—actual or potential frustrators.

3. People who usually arouse only friendly feelings can produce marked aggression under certain circumstances.

As to the inhibition of aggression, Dollard and his co-workers postulate that:

1. The strength of inhibition of any act of aggression increases with the amount of punishment anticipated as a consequence of that act;
   (a) injury to a loved object is punishment,
   (b) anticipation of failure is equivalent to anticipation of punishment.
2. With the strength of *frustration* held constant, the greater the anticipation of *punishment* for a given act of aggression the less apt the act is to occur.
3. With anticipation of *punishment* held constant, the greater the strength of *frustration*, the more apt the act is to occur.

Are these hypotheses valuable in application to every day social problems; or even clinical problems? A person may express his aggression in activity or passivity; individually, in small groups, or in large collectives. He may express his aggression verbally through wit, sarcasm, scorn, obscenity or silence. He may also do so through substituting another emotion toward the frustrating individual. That substitution may be another person, himself, or some symbolic representation such as an inanimate object.

He may discharge his aggressive impulses in games, fights with others, or defiant withdrawal, or through creative sublimations. He may engage in violent rebellion of conscientiously conceived nonviolent protest and just as conscientiously conceived violent protest against presumed frustrators. He may use neurotic substitutions, masochism, depressive symptomatology or schizophrenic withdrawal.

In man,[27] aggression is expressed through ego action. It reveals itself actively in the motives to master, harm, or destroy an object—or through passivity—to be mastered, harmed, or destroyed. Aggression is modified by the ego, because the ego fears it may be endangered by counter actions of the object of aggression, through displacements and restriction of aims, through sublimation, or by fusion with the libidinal drive.

Deprivation and frustration with stimulation of aggression is regarded as necessary for ego growth.[25] Early in life, frustration produces only a diffuse state of rage. That undifferentiated state of tension becomes directed and assumes forms of hostility directed towards others only when the growing infant or child has developed a perceived attachment to another person. Direction of attack is a sign of ego organization, an adaptation of the early diffuse infantile protest.

It means that the aggressive drive is modifiable within the framework of the evolution of human relations and, in that framework, the nurtured child will internalize controls against aggression that will guide him through life, its violent release dependent only upon orders from cultural authority.[31]

From the developmental studies of Redl and Wineman[29] and others,[26, 31, 32] the growing child's ability to internalize controls and structure superego is not the only factor influencing the adult who later defies society through violence. Maldevelopment of ego functioning caused by inadverse nurturing may lead to a repertoire of actions used as shrewd psychological defenses against the moral implications of such acts, even when moral values are comprehended and internalized.

The problem of treatment for those who have undergone such pathologic growth requires the development of new emotional attachments which allow a gradual decrease and exposure of the hostile character defenses and recognition of the already existing internal morality. Experiences that encourage development of those functions necessary to delay gratification are also required to compete and cope effectively with both success and failure, to identify with others, to find pride in skills and to accept one's limitations.

Are there factors today which magnify the sense of frustration in some and increase the potential for aggression? Rates for mental hospitalization, infant mortality, crime, drug addiction and all other indicators of anomie are higher for all groups who live in our urban slums. Here, too, are the centers from which destructive violence has erupted within the past several years and has erupted in other societies for centuries.

Aggression is enhanced in all socio-economic groups through increased crowding and competition for the material advantages of our closing society. Apparently in all species, territorial restriction or competition stimulates the aggressive drive.[8, 13] The aggression of deprived persons today is aggravated too by the exposure of their failure to acquire space, housing, education and health services, or other benefits of a wealthy society. This is made apparent through the voices of our political and business leaders and through every modern audiovisual communicative device—notably television.

As one surveys the clinical experiences of psychiatrists today, there is reason to doubt that we have much to offer other than the theories and observations of our predecessors when it comes to explaining overt expressions of violence. Most psychiatrists are involved in clinic or office practice where they observe only the ritualized and socially acceptable expressions of the aggressive drive. Even those psychiatrists in large mental hospitals now find as their patients those who have been inhibited through chemical treatment and by confinement after an act. Perhaps our child psychiatrists more frequently have the opportunity to observe direct aggression in children and adolescents. Our contribution to society's concern over violence is not to be denied. The observations and hypotheses of our predecessors have bearing on both violence and aggression in terms of individual and collective expressions of the aggressive drive.

As for the collective expressions of violence in mobs, even sociologists lean heavily upon Freud's explanation of group psychology in their search for understanding the dynamics of mob behavior. The amalgamation of psychoanalytic, psychological and sociological viewpoints on mob psychology was achieved well over a decade ago.[33]

As Rose Spiegel[34] puts it, each man maintains "a relationship and a sense of relationship . . . not only to persons in . . . range of interpersonal interaction but to various small and large molecules of society." To her, this universe of relatedness constitutes a parameter of personality which allows the following categorization of violence:

1. "Socially sanctioned or condoned violence": as in wars, personal self-defense, outrage, or crimes of passion in some cultures.
2. "Violence as interactions between the individual and his group, society or government." Here one places the assassinations, collective violence rationalized as ideology by groups as ways of bringing about social change, or violence as gratifications—that of paranoid activity on the social scene.
3. "Violence as an expression of individual, transactional and intra-psychic processes but not oriented to society." Here one places all the deviations of the aggressive drive expressed in characterological abnormality, psychopathologic defense and action.

I wish to comment also on the transformation of a dedicated group into a mob. The dedicated group has as its focus a respected leader. The group leader, whether a charismatic individual dedicated to a high cause, or an individual therapist treating a small number of patients, achieves his position by the transference to him of the parental affection and respect of the group. The group identifies with its perceptions of the leader as though he were a father.

Group therapy may be defeated when this cohesiveness is ruptured by inclusion in the group of a psychopath with a lack of ability to establish an affective attachment to the leader. The simple character neurotic who must defy and destroy the leader, or the psychotic who may respond idiosyncratically and sometimes with violence to the leader, may also disrupt the group.

As psychiatrists we choose for the benefit of the greater number in order to exclude from therapeutic groups those few patients whose presence might destroy the benefits available to others. Separate groups are arranged for such persons.

Most leaders initiate their careers by gathering about them individuals who have within them strong tendencies to identify with that leader's values. In political life, as the leader's success grows in seeking the goals of the original group, so too, his band of followers enlarges. It is here that his potential for control dissipates. And it is here that the knowledge of the great range of human personalities, their weaknesses and strengths become important. Hoffer described the qualities of the mob in "The True Believers"[28] with his characteristic penetration, as follows:

"The poor, the misfits, the guilty, the selfish, the minorities, the sinners, the bored and the ambitious who visualized opportunities in his wake. . . ."

Once a non-violent group has been exposed to violence—and the social psychological studies from the French war and revolution to present times support the observation—then if within the group there is a polarizing focus for its emotional turmoil, no matter what its general character structure, the usual internalized superego controls give way in many persons, and they seem impelled by identification with the mob to act out the impulse of those around them.

Thus, one initial violent act of aggression committed by persons unidentified with the leader—whether consciously directed for political purposes, or unconsciously determined in a brain damaged, psychopathic criminal, neurotic or psychotic mind—may stimulate a vast number to discharge their inner aggression in ways they never conceived.

Many act irresponsibly in a mob because personal responsibility weakens in this situation of anonymity. Others respond to universal identification. As Le Bon, quoted from Brown,[33] stated: "Amongst the most savage members of the French Convention were to be found inoffensive citizens, who, under other circumstances, would have been peaceable notaries or virtuous magistrates."

The extraordinary power of the leader to control antisocial behavior is perhaps less appreciated than it deserves to be. In a sense, the psychiatrist and psychoanalyst hold this position for their coterie of patients. Their interpretations, their actions, or even their omission of interpretations have profound effects upon the social behavior of the patients.

Thus, the leader who exhorts to violent acts, who indicates his expectation of such acts, or who fails to speak against them when social turmoil supports the occurrence of violent collectives, is one who may encourage the translation of verbal aggressiveness into forms of destructive violence. With the knowledge we have of personality functioning and its many variants, we must state that the leader who enjoins mass efforts at such times takes unto himself, even if he preaches nonviolence, the responsibility for every man who joins his march. He needs to have in mind the potential composition of the body of his followers *and* a sense of the extent of his influence upon the *psychopathic fringe* of that body.

Our moral leaders today find themselves in a difficult dilemma. Shall they posit aggression in the form of violence in order to achieve the human liberation of a segment of our population or to oppose war, or shall they just argue verbally against the hypocrisy which still holds a segment of our population in bondage and attempt to complete their task within the frame of existing social codes which have seemed to many of the deprived so impervious to response?

Society in general has the right to raise the question: At what point does the leader himself become an accessory to the acts of violence performed by those who follow him?

The complexity of the problem of violence clearly goes beyond the usual clinical focus of the psychiatrist. What then do psychiatrists have to offer to society in the control of human violence?

We can and must give to significant commissions and individuals at national, state and local levels our knowledge and experience. We must speak up for all those proposals which reduce material and emotional deprivation, the forerunners of personality defect and inadequacy as well as of violent behavior.

We must maintain our traditional role in recognition, treatment and rehabilitation of the violent individual. We must develop more knowledge through active interest in research and bring the skills of our membership to those institutions where the violent accumulate.

Above all we are challenged to teach and use our theoretical skills and experience in the group process to assist the leaders of hitherto passive and deprived groups so that they can effectively direct aggression without promoting senseless violence.

REFERENCES

1. Lorenz, K.: *On Aggression,* Harcourt, Brace & World, Inc., New York, 1966.
2. Coppleson, V.M.: *Shark Attack,* Angus & Robertson, Ltd., Sydney, Australia, 1958.
3. Mickleburgh, W.E.: Med J Aust Suppl 2:1247, 1966.
4. Brosin, H.W.: Hosp & Comm Psychiat 19:18, 1968.
5. Berkowitz, L.: Sci Amer 210:35, 1966.
6. Buss, A.H.: *The Psychology of Aggression,* John Wiley & Son, Inc., 1961.
7. Bychowski, G.: Bull NY Acad Med 43:300, 1967.
8. Carthy, J. and Ebling, F.J.: Nature 11/4915:129, 1964.
9. Eggersten, P.F.: Psychiatry 27:211, 1964.
10. Fried, M., Harris, M. and Murphy, R.: *The Anthropology of Armed Conflict and Aggression,* The Natural Press, Garden City, New York, 1968.
11. McCaldon, R.J.: Canada Psychiat Ass J 9:502, 1964.
12. Rifkin, S.H.: Science 140:904, 1963.
13. Scott, J.P.: *Aggression.* Univ. Chicago Press, Chicago, 1958.
14. Kolb, L.C.: Noyes Modern Clinical Psychiatry, 7th ed. W.B. Saunders Co., Philadelphia, 1
15. Abrahamsen, D.: Bull NY Acad Med 43:861, 1967.
16. Mark, V.H.: Med Opinion Rev 4:26, 1968.
17. Wertham, F.: The Show of Violence. Doubleday, Garden City, N.Y., 1949.
18. Bruch, H.: Cm J Psych 124:693, 1967.
19. Goltz
20. Bard, Mountcastle and other
21. Valzelli, L.: Advances Pharmacol 5:79, 1967.
22. Cohen, M., Freedman, N., Englechardt, D.M. and Margolis, R.A.: Arch Gen Psychiat 19:50, 1968.
23. Laing, R.D.: Int J Soc Psychol 10:184, 1964.
24. Rappaport, J.R., Ed.: *The Clinical Evaluation of the Dangerousness of the Mentally Ill,* Charles C. Thomas, Springfield, Ill. 1967.
25. Brosin, H.W.: *Aggression and Defense; Neural Mechanisms and Social Patterns* (Brain Function, Vol. 5), Eds. Clemente, C.D. and Lindsley, D.B., Univ. of Cal. Press, Los Angeles, 267, 1967.
26. Freud: Psychoanal Stud Child 3:37, 1949.
27. Hartmann, H., Dris, E. and Lowenstein, R.M.: Psychoanal Stud Child 3:0, 1949.
28. Hoffer, E.: The True Believers, Harper-Row, New York, 1951.
29. Redl, F. and Wineman, D.: Children Who Hate. The Disorganization and Breakdown of Behavior Concepts, Free Press, Glencoe, Ill. 1951.
30. Dollard, J., Dobb, L.W., Miller, N.E., Mawrer, C.H. and Sears, R.R.: *Frustration and Aggression,* Yale Univ. Press, New Haven, Conn., 1939.
31. Rank, B.: Psychoanal Stud Child 3:43, 1949.
32. Eissler, K.R.: *Searchlights on Delinquency,* Int Universities Press, New York, 1949.
33. Brown, R.W.: *Handbook of Social Psychology,* Ed. Gardner Lindzey, 3(23):833, Addison-Wesley Pub. Co., Cambridge, 1954.
34. Spiegel, R.: Int Jahrbuch zur Weiterentwicklung der psychoanalyse 3:122, 1968.

TOWARD A THEORY OF
COLLECTIVE VIOLENCE

John P. Spiegel, M.D.

In our search for appropriate ways to define the main features of an historical epoch we often use the big, broadside label. Thus, the 18th century is called the "Age of Reason," the early 19th century the "Age of Romanticism," and the late 19th century the "Age of Materialism." Continuing this imagery into the 20th century, we can, with some plausibility, characterize more recent times in terms of 30-year periods.

The period from 1900 to 1930 could be called, for the United States at any rate, the "Age of Optimism," reflecting such self-confident national slogans as "manifest destiny" and "make the world safe for democracy." It was a time when, despite the temporary inconvenience of war, depression, or race riots, change always seemed to be for the best.

In contrast, the period from 1930 to 1960 has been called the "Age of Anxiety." Because of the Great Depression, the rise of Fascism, World War II, the collapse of the colonial powers, and the uneasy tension between the Communist and non-Communist worlds, national self-confidence was replaced with increasing self-doubt. Social change seemed to be sometimes out of control and frequently for the worse. Though traces of hope remained attached to such worldwide efforts of reconstruction as the United Nations, the newly emerging nations, and aid to underdeveloped countries, the national mood was one of uncertainty and personal anxiety.

Since 1960, however, the increased turbulence both within and between nations, has introduced a new note into national life—anger, recrimination and aggressive behavior between individuals and groups. A corresponding change in national self-awareness gives rise to the notion that we are at this moment living in the "Age of Violence." Certainly, such a designation is suggested by the expressed concerns in the public media, in political oratory, and in the

---

Dr. Spiegel is director of the Lemberg Center for the Study of Violence, Brandeis University, Waltham, Massachusetts.

minds of citizens troubled by campus riots, civil disorder and the fear of violence in the streets.

Although we may be reasonable, from the viewpoint of national imagery, in calling the period we are passing through an Age of Violence, the title may not be necessarily accurate nor helpful. In fact, it raises many questions. What is meant by the word "violence?" What moral or ethical assumptions are embedded in such a characterization? What social and psychological processes can account for an increase in personal and collective aggression, if indeed such an increase can actually be demonstrated?

I shall attempt some partial and temporary answers to these questions.

During the so-called Age of Anxiety, a good deal of psychosomatic and psychiatric research was based on the concept of "stress," an internally experienced correlate of anxiety. Similarly, in the sociological and anthropological literature considerable emphasis was placed on processes of integration and equilibrium within social systems. Social change and the pathologies of social systems, if considered at all, were treated as instances of social "strain" to be overcome by a process of internal readjustment.

But in the current, somewhat more heated climate of research, both psychological and social research have shifted, in some degree, to more externally defined problems of behavior. Where individual behavior is concerned, there is an increased focus on drug use and abuse, on hippies and youthful activists or rebels, and on the relation of the person to his family, organizational or community environment. At the social level, interest has shifted to a greater examination of social problems and the need for social change. Concurrently, we are acutely aware that we lack not only knowledge for determining desirable directions of such change, but also the techniques for bringing change about.

Although the shift from internal to external problems, and from adjustment to reality to changing that reality, should not be overemphasized, this transformation does highlight the need for new definitions and concepts. Just as, during the 30's and 40's, it was necessary to define "stress" and "anxiety" as accurately as possible, now it is of the greatest importance to define "aggression" and "violence."

All definitions tend to sound dry and academic. Nevertheless, significant consequences flow from them. Although "violence" may be defined narrowly or broadly, we have chosen a narrow definition as follows: Violence lies at the extreme end of a spectrum of aggressive behavior. It is characterized by acts of physical force aimed at the severe injury or destruction of persons, objects or organizations. A second defining feature is concerned with timing and tempo, usually expressed as "explosiveness." Violent behavior, in other words, is aggression released fully and abruptly, usually in a state of high energy arousal.

The definition rules out many behaviors often included when the word occurs in ordinary speech or in the popular press. For example, it excludes sin and evil in general as well as such particular forms of evil as injustice, exploitation, deprivation, defamation and starvation. It excludes brutalizing social arrangements not characterized by the use of physical force.

Many persons, particularly social activists, are unhappy with such a limited definition. For example, they prefer to describe our society as violent because it is responsible for so much social injustice. From the point of view of research, however, it seems preferable to restrict the behavior to be studied and to ask that other forms of undesirable social behavior, such as injustice and exploitation, be considered separately.

A more serious problem arising from the narrow definition concerns destructive force used in lower-keyed or non-explosive ways; for example, torture, poisoning and exile. Such acts could be conceived as lying within the spectrum of aggressive behavior just short of violence. A graphic or linear concept of this sort, however, becomes quite arbitrary in the absence of a definition of aggression, and we all know how difficult it has been, in the past, to define "aggression."

Despite the difficulties, the need for a workable concept of aggression geared to the concept of violence is so great that it seems important to formulate a definition for this purpose. Accordingly, the following is proposed:

Aggression is behavior involving the use of force or its symbolic equivalent to effect an outcome in line with the intentions, or goals, of the aggressor acting against the intentions or goals of an adversary. It usually, but not always, occurs in an agonistic situation characterized by a conflict of interests.

This definition is by design quite broad. It leaves open the character, intensity and aim of the force used to secure compliance from an opponent. Under these general terms, aggression can vary along a continuum from acts of simple assertion requiring a minimal use of force, at one pole, to violence, as defined above, at the other.

The definition also leaves open the techniques—such as a formal challenge, a surprise attack or a conspiracy—used to set up adversary relations. Finally, it leaves open the timing of the behavior with respect to securing compliance or non-compliance. For example, the show of real or symbolic force to secure compliance in advance of a struggle we call threat-behavior, just as we call force used after the loss of a contest revenge.

Two significant consequences proceed from this formulation. First, a great deal of aggressive behavior is non-violent in character. Even in the purely physical realm, such acts as pushing, holding, blocking, restraining, constraining, confining, and depriving, though aggressive, are non-violent. Considering the heated debates over who has done what to whom in the streets of our cities and on our college campuses, it is of the greatest importance to distinguish between violence, on the one hand, and aggression, no matter how disruptive, on the other.

The second consequence consists of an avoidance of the question of whether aggression is to be regarded as instinctual or learned behavior. It must represent a combination of both elements. Man as the killer-ape, struggling to control his innate violence, or man as the noble savage taught to be violent by an aggressive civilization—such troublesome images become irrelevant.

Aggression as the use of force to overcome obstacles is innate behavior that man shares with most living species. Violence as the maximum arousal of aggression for destructive purposes, including the killing of members of one's own species, is by the same token, an innate behavior potentially capable of being aroused in all men. But the internal, biological conditions necessary for arousal are ordinarily under the control of external, environmental contingencies.

If this view is correct, then what is sorely needed is research to investigate the feedback relations between the mechanisms of biological arousal, particularly in childhood, and the environmental controls, both instigating and inhibiting, over aggressive behavior.

Clearly, the first level of environmental control over the behavior of man is based on morality and ethics. Ethical standards govern what is regarded as acceptable or inacceptable behavior, both for the individual and the group. Our question, then, must be: Is there an ethics of violence, known and subscribed to by most members of our society—or, perhaps more cogently—by members of the world societies?

Despite an abundance of ethical statements from a variety of religious and philosophical contexts, there exists no systematic analysis of ethical principles in this area. What does exist, apparently, is a vast confusion—a state of contradiction bordering on chaos—which has been more or less internalized by most members of our society.

Three ethical, or quasi-ethical positions can be discerned within the confusion. The first position can be called positive and negative "absolutism." It is taken by persons who say either that violence is never justified, the negative position, or that violence in the pursuit of political goals is always justified, the positive position.

A moral posture of negative absolutism is quite familiar to Americans under the label of "pacifism." It is also the position of Quakers and some other religious sects: violence between nations, groups, or individuals is *never,* under any circumstances, justified.

A positive ethics of violence is not so directly known to Americans, but it has been well articulated by Sorel, the French social philosopher, who postulated that violence is a social good:[1] those who are fit to govern are those who understand and know how to use violence; the ability to employ violence intelligently is what separates the elite of any historical epoch from the dull, passive, decadent and corrupt bourgeoisie. Hitler, with his boast, "We *are* savages; we're proud of being savages!" was an intellectual offspring of Sorel, as was Mussolini with his advocacy of national "audacity," along with the Italian poet and political adventurer Gabriele D'Annunzio, both of whom emphasized the creative, releasing functions of violence, daring and militant pugnacity.

In contrast to such absolutist positions, most Americans tend to endorse a relative one. According to relativist principles, violence is generally condemned but can be justified under certain conditions—for example, in the service of "self-defense." Violence in behalf of an indisputably just cause—for example, a "war of national liberation"—is another possible basis of exemption. The guiding principle is flexibility: permission to use violence depends upon conditions, although there often is a notable lack of consensus as to which conditions can serve as an excuse for violence.

The paralyzing effects of confusion and contradiction are nowhere more conspicuous than in the confrontation of absolutist and relativist ethical principles. From the point of view of the relativist, the absolute position is exceedingly dangerous. How would any individual or group ever overcome injustice, escape exploitation or overcome oppression, if violence were not permitted?

As far as a positive ethical position is concerned, to the relativist this posture seems to promote perpetual destruction and killing, as pugnacious aggressors flex their muscles and deploy their weaponry against each other, utterly without moral controls, in a state of constant vendetta.

But, to the absolutist, the relativist position seems equally dangerous; like a rubber band, it can be indefinitely stretched and extended to justify continuous escalations of violence. Today we have to fight in a just cause in Vietnam, tomorrow in China—the day after that the whole Communist world? If we exonerate ghetto rioters on the basis of "white racism" in Watts, won't the violence break out in Dayton, in Newark, in Detroit?

To such blind alleys and fallouts of communication at the overtly moral level we must add a new component of environmental control: the recently articulated "therapeutic" positions. Here again we encounter an unyielding contradiction between positive and negative positions. The negative therapeutic position holds that an individual or a society displays violence because of illness. The violent society is a "sick" society; the violent person is disturbed. Thus professional help, either on the part of psychiatrists or social therapists, is required.

The positive therapeutic position, on the other hand, holds that violence itself is therapeutic, a position clearly articulated by the black psychiatrist, Fanon.[2] An oppressed people, or an inferiorized person, according to this view, will usually identify with the aggressor and, as an inevitable result, display depression, apathy and alienation. If, however, identification *of* the aggressor is substituted for identification *with* the aggressor, then the victim will fight the oppressor, and overcome both his depression and his social inferiority.

This contradiction of guiding principles again generates seemingly insoluble problems. From the viewpoint of the positive therapeutic principle, the negative position is both degrading and unrealistic. What is to become of our national heroes if violence is a sign of illness? Was George Washington "sick" because he led the violent action which freed our nation from the English Crown? Were the colonies "sick" because they fought the British at Lexington and Concord?

To those who subscribe to the negative therapeutic position, however, the positive position seems a prescription for paranoia. How is a sense of reality to be established if any frustration or grievance or feeling of inferiority is to be ascribed to some real or fictitious oppressor? Doesn't this position sanction a wild spree of impulse gratification? Of the fight of all against all?

There appears to be no way of reconciling these moral contradictions. Ethical principles, it would seem, can be found to justify almost any line of conduct. Perhaps this means that morality and its embodiment in law is a primitive, or at least a prescientific, form of social control. If so, then we obviously must search for more rational or objective principles of environmental control. But is research, specifically in this case behavioral research, actually prepared to assume such a responsibility?

We may be able to shed light on this question by examining the conditions under which collective violence breaks out, confining our attention to civil disorders rather than full-scale war or revolution. Since the Stamp Act Riot in 1765, the country has undergone seven cycles of civil disorder. Each cycle was characterized by a number of similar instances of violent uprisings occurring in various parts of the nation.

Shay's Rebellion in 1786, a revolt of poor farmers in the western frontier of Massachusetts, exemplifies the first cycle. The farmers were resentful of the unjust tax laws passed by the Massachusetts Legislature. Led by Daniel Shays, they seized the law courts to prevent the legal apparatus from functioning. The wealthy members of the Legislature, not realizing how angry the disenfranchised farmers had become, were surprised and frightened. As we say today, the power structure got the message and passed fairer tax laws. Similar uprisings were to occur in other parts of the Eastern seaboard; usually with a successful outcome.

The second cycle of civil disorder consisted of attacks by Protestants against Irish-Catholics during the 1840's and 1850's. Led by the Native American Party, the Protestant establishment vilified Irish-Americans as papists and unpatriotic foreigners. Catholic churches and schools were burned. In Philadelphia, the city of brotherly love, 24 persons were killed and more than 100 were wounded during an anti-Catholic riot in July 1844. In Charlestown, a convent was burned to the ground.

The Civil War Draft Riots of 1863 constituted the third cycle of disorders. Angered by the exemption clause of the Conscription Act, which permitted the wealthy to escape the draft by the payment of $300, poor people rose up in wrath against the Republican Party and the police who were called upon to keep order. Although motivations were mixed and there were vicious attacks upon black people, who were held responsible for the war, the principle cause of the disorders was an intense feeling of injustice.

The fourth cycle, the West Coast anti-Chinese riots, began in the 1870's. Among California's poor white population racism combined with fear of economic threat to identify "the Chinese Menace" as a social problem requiring violent solution. During the riot in Los Angeles in October 1871, 23 Chinese were killed. Similar riots occurred in 1877 in San Francisco, in 1881 in Denver, and in 1885 in Rock Springs.

The fifth riot cycle, the long series of disorders arising from the movement of organized labor, began in the 1870's, reached a peak of intensity in the 1890's, and disappeared only after passage of the National Labor Relations legislation in the 1940's. Thirty-five persons were killed and hundreds were wounded in the Carnegie Steel plant strike at Homestead, Pa. in July 1892. During the Pullman strike in June and July 1894, a total of 16,000 Federal troops were called out to control the disorders which, starting in Illinois, spread out over the country from Indiana to California.

The sixth cycle, the anti-Negro riots before, during and after World War I, were perhaps the bloodiest and cruelest of the series. In East St. Louis, Chicago and elsewhere, while policemen stood by and National Guardsmen joined in the attack, whites viciously assailed Negroes. They clubbed, shot and hanged any black person they could catch. As in the West Coast anti-Chinese disturbances, racism was combined with economic fears, and whites tried to drive black men, women and children out of the neighborhood, out of the city, out of their way.

Since 1964 we have been engaged in the seventh cycle of disorders, involving black people seeking control of their ghetto communities, and young people seeking more control over their own lives in their college communities. Though there has been less violence in this seventh cycle, fewer deaths and fewer injuries, the same themes of injustice, protest and backlash which made themselves felt in the previous cycles are apparent in the current sequence.

Has the substance of this protest varied over the years, or has the underlying problem remained the same, despite its different manifestations? If we are to be concerned with the conditions governing the outbreak of collective disorder, this is an extremely important question.

The evidence would seem to suggest that all the riot cycles have been correlated with a chronic social conflict, a basic flaw in the social structure of the United States. In a previous communication,[3] I described this strain as the incompatibility between our democratic ideals and our authoritarian practices. The rights of man, the equality among peoples, and the principle of representative government, the main items in the democratic ideology, have been pitted from the time of the Constitutional Convention in 1787 against an all-encompassing but largely masked authoritarianism modeled after the European social systems that the American Revolution was presumed to have overthrown. This concealed hierarchical structure of power has been maintained in two ways: (1) by the principle of exclusion of social groups from the decision-making process; and (2) by the operation of pyramidal, bureaucratic structures with power centered at the top of the pyramid.

At the time of its formation, the American system of government was limited by six principles of inclusion and exclusion. Let us call this the WAMPAM structure of the social system. In order to have access to power one had to be:

(1) White, excluding all who were red, yellow, or black;

(2) Anglo-Saxon or of some closely related national background, excluding the Irish, the southern and central Europeans, and those from the Middle and Far East;

(3) Middle-class or better, excluding the working class and the poor;

(4) Protestant, excluding all Catholics, Moslems and Jews;

(5) Adult, excluding all children and youth from the decision-making process; and

(6) Male, excluding all females of whatever color, religion, or national background.

This was the political and social structure of our republic. Whether a system so elitist in form and function could be called a democracy is doubtful. From the beginning these six structural principles were under attack from both sides—by the "reconstructivists" who wanted to broaden them, and by the "nativists" who thought they already were too broad. All the riot cycles, including the present one, can be correlated with attempts by one or another excluded group to penetrate the elitist barrier in order to be admitted to the seats of power.

In Shays' Rebellion, the poor began their struggle, one that has not yet been wholly successful. The anti-Catholic riots were meant to discourage the Irish from their bid for power, feeble as it was during the 1840's. In the Civil War draft riots the poor and the Irish joined forces to limit the power of the wealthier Protestant establishment over the conscription issue. And so it went for the orientals in California, for labor organizations all over the industrial north, and for black people in both the north and the south. A relatively weak reconstructivist effort to enter the system was almost invariably met by a powerful and violent nativist effort to keep them out.

With the single exception of the draft riots, a more complicated case in any event, reconstructivists have directed their violence mainly against property, such as buildings, equipment and machinery. Nativists, on the other hand, have tended to direct their violence against persons, quite often in the form of frenzied and bloody massacres. Nativists have consistently held that the reconstructivists "provoked" the violence, usually through nonviolent demonstrations and protests, which were conveniently found to be illegal or simply annoying.

Though particular reconstructivist efforts have been successful, they have not succeeded in changing the system. Irish and Italians, Jews and Catholics have been admitted into the power structure in ever greater numbers. Still, the reconstructivists of one season become the nativists of the next.

Irish-Catholics, Jews and members of labor unions, forgetting the bitter struggles of their past, now resent the efforts of the poor, the blacks and the youth to enter the system and make their claim for power. The familiar objections of the past are leveled at each new group knocking loudly at the elitist barrier with their ever-present "demands." They are seen as upstarts, as unintelligent, unmotivated, lazy, untrainable, unmannerly, uncouth, and, above all, undeserving. The stamp of inferiority is pressed upon them, softened, to be sure, by humanitarian kindness, Christian forebearance or therapeutic understanding. But to the excluded, a patronizing charity is little better, and may well be worse, than a last-ditch rejection.

This description may have been slightly overstated. Not all reconstructivists have turned nativistic after entering the system. There have always been some who, after having climbed the upper rungs of the social ladder, stretched down their hands to help those at the bottom of the heap, sometimes at considerable risk to their own positions. But such rescue operations, even when successful, have not changed the vertically stratified structure of the social system. They seem mainly to add new rungs at the bottom of the ladder.

When considering the conversion of reconstructivists into nativists in a previous publication,[3] I asked why such a transformation should take place. What psychological mechanisms, other than identification with the aggressor, could account for such a seemingly radical change?

Before their penetration into the system, reconstructivists of whatever historical epoch have usually been interested in adding their own cultural forms —their art, their speech patterns, their national heroes and holidays—to the native American stock of culture patterns. Such efforts have always been strongly resisted by the nativists. To them, a broadening of this sort has meant a weakening, an introduction of un-American clannishness, at the least, corrupting of the moral fibre of the country, and, at the most, threatening a "take-over" of the entire nation.

Thus, in the 1840's rumors were propagated by the Native American Party that the Catholic church, including the Pope, was planning to take over the country. In the 1890's, and again in the early 1920's radical labor leaders—anarchists, syndicalists, socialists, or Communists—were represented as planning the take-over. Today, radical youth and extremist student leaders are reported to be planning the destruction of the country in order to seize power.

Let us grant that in the minds of a few revolutionaries these have been serious goals. Still, revolutionary or drastic change never has been a serious threat in our country. Therefore, we must ask: how is it that, having had first-hand experience with the unrealistic nature of nativist fears, newly arrived reconstructivists can so quickly internalize these apocalyptic fantasies and direct them at the newest ranks of dissatisfied outcasts?

After much discussion and thought about this question, I have concluded that it has probably been wrongly posed. Rather than assuming that a change takes place, would we not be more correct to assume no change at all? On this view, reconstructivists have all along only wanted "a piece of the action," as it is phrased today. They have wished to penetrate the system but not to change it. In the process, to be sure, they have wanted to bring parts of their culture along while dropping or attenuating other parts. But, in the main, they have wanted to become as Americanized as possible as quickly as possible, to be given the chance of "making it" within the system as they have found it.

This would imply an easy acceptance, once entry was gained, of both the democratic ideological disguise and the authoritarian realities of the social system. If this is true, their protest all along was directed not at the elitist system *per se*, but at their own exclusion from it.

If the foregoing analysis is correct, then our initial question concerning the conditions governing the outbreak of collective violence becomes terribly poignant. Large-scale civil disorder, it now appears, will erupt whenever a group in an excluded category makes its historically appropriate bid for entry into the elitist system.

There are, of course, particular determining conditions governing the local outbreaks of rioting. These have been dealt with in the Kerner Commission Report[4] and in previous publications from the Lemberg Center for the Study of Violence. But in general the environmental contingencies associated with the violence arise from the clash between a determined reconstructivist campaign and an equally determined nativist resistance. Since the resulting cycles of disorder produce no change in the underlying social conflict, their recurrence is inevitable.

Given our open immigration policy, and omitting for the moment the almost intractable problem of color, new ethnic and national groups will continue to obtain a foothold in the country, to undergo exclusion and inferiorization, and eventually a new cycle of disorder. There would seem to be no solution.

Recently, however, as if in response to such a pessimistic conclusion, various groups have pointed with increasing urgency to the need for dealing with the underlying social conflict. It is being suggested that what is usually talked about as social change, even rapid social change, is in fact an example of *Plus ça change, plus c'est la même chose.* For the most part, suggestions for real rather than delusory change are concerned with the need for remodeling the social and political structures which support the elitist system. While such a restructuring is of the greatest importance, current blueprints being offered for this purpose suffer from a certain vagueness combined with angry denunciations of the status quo. The New Left and militant student groups appear more certain about what is wrong than how to make things better.

It seems quite possible that the predominantly negative tone and the absence of positive models of change may be due to the neglect of the impact of cultural values on the very structures which need changing. The work of sociologists and cultural anthropologists has produced fairly convincing evidence that cultural value orientations and social institutions have reciprocal effects. Studies which I have carried out with Kluckhohn on family structure and function, using her theory of variations in value orientations, have demonstrated the importance of these interrelationships to family conflicts.[5] It seems fruitful, therefore, to submit the chronic conflict between democratic and authoritarian values in our society to a more refined value and analysis based on the Kluckhohn theoretical approach.

Of the five value orientation categories included in the Kluckhohn schema, only one, the *relational* orientation will be described. Although the *relational* category is probably of key significance, I must stress that a full discussion of the current social conflict would require reference to all five categories.

The *relational* value category deals with the issues I have discussed under the labels of democratic and authoritarian values but in a more complex fashion. It is concerned with the manner in which group decisions are arrived at and with the ordering of interpersonal relations within the group. Three possible arrangements for group decision-making are specified by the theory: the individual, the collateral, and the lineal.

Individualism is an arrangement in which each member of the group has the right—indeed, the obligation—to state his opinion and the decision is made by a vote of the majority. In the collateral arrangement effort is directed at reaching group consensus by a decision with which most group members can feel comfortable. In the lineal arrangement decisions are made by the leader, then handed down through the chain of authority.

The interpersonal aspects of the three arrangements are consonant with the decision-making process. In lineal structures, each member must know his place in a system of leaders and followers featuring dominance and submission. Strict dependence on the hierarchy of authority is strongly emphasized. In collateral arrangements, group harmony is stressed. Group members are mainly at an equal level of importance; but, the goals of the group are more important than individual needs or preferences. Individualism accents the importance of each member, of his own goals and needs, of his ability to make decisions by himself and to stand on his own two feet.

The Kluckhohn theory assumes that every culture or subculture ranks the three arrangements in an order of preference in accordance with its institutions. The ranking pattern which is dominantly preferred in the United States is first the individual, second collateral, and third lineal. This pattern has been ascertained in several ways, but primarily through the use of questionnaire schedules. It is clearly a value pattern which is easily articulated—a set of preferences closest to conscious awareness.

The importance of the individual conforms to the ideal image Americans have of themselves. For certain purposes, however, they will shift to the second-order collateral position, as in the case of team sports, or in a crisis when individualism must be subordinated to group goals. The least preferred lineal position receives short shrift. While it might be necessary in certain situations, most Americans resent a boss who acts too bossy and their sympathies tend to lie with those who have to take rather than give orders.

Although there are many subcultural groups which vary from this pattern of relational values, there is no doubt about its stability for the nation as a whole when respondents are asked to make verbal choices among alternatives. How then are we to reconcile this pattern, especially its anti-authoritarian implications, with the authoritarian practices and the hierarchy of power which we noted earlier?

The first answer which suggests itself is that this value pattern conforms to the official, democratic ideology of the nation. It corresponds to the well-advertised American way of life, a view with which we have been inculcated from early childhood. Because it is so strongly held among our ego-ideals, we tend selectively to screen out, to repress, or to dismiss most evidence to the contrary in our national affairs, or everyday experience. We are forced to falsify our own experiences and to maintain the hypocrisy which the young, who are not yet committed to inauthenticity, so easily spot in adult behavior.

Furthermore, this official pattern of values receives just enough valid support in middle-class styles of life, particularly within the family, so that it is not wholly lacking in substance. Thus we can afford, it seems, though at considerable psychological cost, to shut our eyes to the entrenched lineality that characterizes our political institutions, our universities and hospitals, our business and commercial establishments, and our conduct of foreign affairs.

But there is a more subtle and more unconscious fashion in which the discrepancy between ideology and reality is obscured. Individualism was first installed as a national value during the Revolutionary War to rationalize the declaration of independence from the Crown. "All men are created equal," said Thomas Jefferson, and "are endowed with certain inalienable rights." Among those rights were life, liberty, and the pursuit of happiness.

To justify the obtaining of liberty, individualism had to be elevated into the highest position, while lineality, which would have required loyalty to the King, had to be reduced. Collaterality, the value principle that united the colonies in common effort, was hardly mentioned in Jefferson's eloquent prose. The struggle was between tyranny—that is lineality—and liberty—that is, individualism.

The value goals of the Founding Fathers were valid, for their time. But the formula of freedom versus tyranny in the absence of a strong collateral value orientation too easily becomes a mask for the perpetuation of tyranny.

Almost every dictator has used the language of freedom to obtain power. Freedom from something, from the conqueror, from the sense of inferiority, from want, from lawlessness, becomes the slogan to rationalize the seizing of power for the purpose of subjugating someone else.

Identification with the oppressor perpetuates the authoritarianism of the fighter for freedom. The lineal principle, the unconscious or concealed endorsement of authoritarianism, persists behind the mask of individualism. The institutions established in the name of freedom embody for the most part the hierarchical structuring of authority. Thus it seems fair to say that the *operative* pattern of relational preferences consists first of the individual, second the lineal, and third collateral. This is, of course, in conflict with the officially acknowledged, or *ideal* ranking pattern: individualism first, collateral second, and lineal third. It is the inconsistency between the ideal and operative pattern that generates the strain in the system.

It has been said that the price of liberty is eternal vigilance. Vigilance against tyranny, of course. But this saying misses the mark. It seems more likely that any price-mark attached to liberty would have to be labeled "collaterality." Angry demands for the rights of an individual, or a group, would not be necessary if social structures were arranged horizontally rather than vertically—if all were in the same boat, on the same level.

In the presence of pyramidal power structures neither vigilance nor protest can do much to preserve freedom. The most that can be accomplished is the effecting of "deals" and "trade-offs" between the power structures—the formation of temporary coalitions which gain a measure of freedom for participating groups. This is the "wheeling and dealing" which runs straight through our political and commercial life. The saying, "You can't fight City Hall," may or may not be true—truer in Chicago, for example, than in New York—but it illustrates the impenetrability of the pyramidal power structure.

The remedy, at the level of cultural value orientations, would seem, then, to consist of a rearrangement of the operative value priorities. Collateral values will have to be given preference over lineality, in action, in the actual performance of our institutions, so that the operative pattern conforms to the ideal pattern. This requirement is hardly a new thought.

The United Nations, the One World Movement, the slogans "Participatory Democracy" and "Community Control"—to say nothing of time-honored appeals to the brotherhood of man—all represent structural rearrangements based on the collateral principle. There may be something to be gained, however, by spelling out the needed direction of change in value terms. At least, this approach can provide a test for determining whether a proposed change really meets the need. Beyond this, it may provide a steady image for the mobilization of the energy required to effect change.

I have raised the question of whether research can provide us with the information needed to determine directions of social change. If the above analysis is correct, then we can give a positive answer to the question. I also questioned whether behavioral research could have something to say about the techniques of change, especially on the score of nonviolent as opposed to violent techniques. This still seems to me more problematical.

Any determined effort to remodel our social structures promoting collaterality over lineality will meet strong resistance. It will be called "collectivism" among many other epithets. Those who propose it will be perceived by many, particularly the nativists, as un-American. Still, collateral structures may contain the resistance by including their opponents in the collateral group. This possibility must be put aside for more study. For the moment, it is sufficient if we have been able to throw some light on the environmental conditions which give rise to outbreaks of collective violence. How to change those conditions must remain a problem for the future.

REFERENCES

1. Sorel, Georges: *Reflections on Violence;* New York, Collier-McMillan, 1961.
2. Fanon, Franz: *The Wretched of the Earth; New York,* Grove Press, 1965.
3. Spiegel, J.P.: "Psychosocial Factors in Riots-Old and New," in American Journal of Psychiatry 125 (3):281, 1968.
4. Kerner, Otto, National Advisory Commission on Civil Disorders; *Report of the National*

Advisory Commission on Civil Disorders; Washington, D.C.; U. S. Gov't Printing Office, March, 1968.

5. Kluckhohn, Florence, and Strodtbeck, Fred: *Variations in Value Orientation;* Rowe Peterson; Evanston, Illinois, 1961.

PSYCHOLOGICAL ASPECTS OF INTERNATIONAL VIOLENCE

Jerome D. Frank, M.D.

Group conflict is a law of life and the chief instigator of violence. The threat of violence, with occasional resort to violence to keep the threat credible, plays an important role in maintaining social order. Through it the weak gain concessions from the powerful before they are driven to desperation, and the rulers maintain order.

In healthy societies the actual display of violence is rare, and threats are largely symbolic. The vote, for example, can be viewed as a substitute for a fight in that it is a test of strength, determining which side would probably win in a battle. Moreover, order is maintained by institutions in which all members of the society have confidence. These institutions, operating under a code of laws, adjudicate power struggles and protect the loser.

Under some conditions of conflict however, violence can get out of hand, and humans resort to the most powerful engines of destruction at their disposal. All that has saved mankind from destruction by such means so far has been the inefficiency of even the most powerful weapons. With the creation in the past few years of enormously deadly biological and chemical poisons and, of course, nuclear weapons, this safeguard has been removed.

Humans are group creatures and the group, not the individual, is the survival unit. When the group is threatened, individual members are expected to sacrifice their lives in its defense and are motivated to do so. In this, humans differ not at all from baboons, and are not too different from ants.

Thus, paradoxical as it may seem, the greatest threat to human survival is not selfishness but altruism. It is the threat to the group of which one is a member, not to oneself, which evokes the most powerful aggressive response. Advocates of non-violence can easily accept death for themselves rather than attack their opponent, but find it much harder to defend their non-violent

Dr. Frank is professor of psychiatry at The Johns Hopkins University School of Medicine, Baltimore, Maryland. This paper also appears in amplified form as "Human Group Aggression," Chapter 22-B, *Biology of Populations;* Sladen and Bang (eds.), American Elsevier Pub. Co., Inc.; New York, N.Y.

position when the threatened victim is a wife or daughter. In this, too, humans resemble animals, who fight especially viciously to defend their young.

But humans add a unique dimension to their allegiance to the group, through their capacity for what Arthur Koestler has termed "self-transcendence." The human group gains the allegiance of its members not only because it is the biological survival unit, but because it embodies and preserves certain ideals, values and symbols. When Kamikaze pilots committed suicide for their emperor, they had more in mind than the little man sitting on the throne of Japan; and when men offer up their lives for the Flag or the Cross, it is for the concepts these bits of cloth or wood represent. Even an abstraction as vague as "a better world for our grandchildren" may suffice to call forth the supreme sacrifice.

Group conflict arises when each group perceives its goal as achievable only at another's expense. Domestically, this type of conflict becomes violent when groups feel intolerably frustrated or threatened, and have lost faith in the institutions of society to satisfy their claims or to protect them.

Thus, in the United States today many blacks have lost faith in the ability or desire of the white community to satisfy their legitimate aspirations; and many whites fear that their jobs, home and lives are jeopardized by militant blacks, and that law enforcement agencies can no longer protect them. As a result both sides have taken to arms.

A main source of resistance to gun registration is the fear of some groups that they will be unilaterally disarmed and thereby left at the mercy of their enemies. In his Presidential campaign, Governor Wallace spoke of the good people giving up their guns and the bad people keeping theirs. Blacks express fears that if they register their guns, they will be disarmed and the whites will not.

Analogously on the international scene, violence erupts when nations find themselves in conflict and cannot appeal to any supranational institution to resolve the issue, and each perceives yielding to the other as a threat to its survival.

Groups in conflict for any length of time regularly form images of each other as enemies, and the enemy image is remarkably similar, no matter who the conflicting parties are.

This is illustrated by the findings of repeated surveys of Americans concerning their characterizations of people of other countries. In 1942 and again in 1966 respondents were asked to choose from a list of adjectives those that best described the people of Russia, Germany and Japan.[1] In 1942 the first five adjectives chosen to characterize both Germans and Japanese (enemies) included warlike, treacherous and cruel, none of which appeared among the first five describing the Russians (allies).

In 1966 all three adjectives had disappeared from American characterizations of the Germans and Japanese (allies) but now the Russians (no longer allies, although more rivals than enemies) were warlike and treacherous. Data were reported for the Mainland Chinese only in 1966, and predictably, they were seen as warlike, treacherous and sly.

The adjectives applied to the Japanese and Germans as war-time enemies no doubt accurately described their behavior—as they do that of all nations at war, including the United States—but it is noteworthy that Americans did not apply these adjectives to the Russians when they were allies, although the Germans undoubtedly saw them as warlike and treacherous, and that Americans now use these terms for the Russians and the Chinese although there is no direct evidence that they apply. The Russians have been talking and acting with great restraint and Chinese bellicosity is restricted to words; neither nation has shown any particular signs of treachery.

The characteristics of the enemy image have been most extensively studied with respect to the United States and the Soviet Union. A detailed content analysis of selected mass and elite publications in these nations a few years ago found that virtually all of the relevant items described the national goal of the other as military expansion, and described the other's military doctrine as including a pre-emptive strike. About two-thirds of the publications in each country believed that negotiations were possible, but could be successful only if "our" side were stronger. A majority saw foreign aid given by their country as motivated by altruism; foreign aid offered by the other side they saw as being in the service of expansionism.[2]

These results are supported by many reports of personal interviews, some systematic and some informal. One of the latter by an American scientist who had the opportunity for a long conversation with a Russian counterpart is worth quoting:

The Westerner regards the Russians as controlled, for the most part without their knowledge, by an oligarchy of rapacious and malevolent men who seek constantly to foment world revolution. The Russian is equally convinced that the West (which means really America, for in Russian eyes all other Western countries are American satellites) is being victimized by a small group of profit-mad 'monopolists' who pull the strings that control government, press and radio and who try to instigate wars in order to sell munitions. On the level of informal conversations such as ours it was impossible to resolve this difference in viewpoint. Each of us was repeating what he had read in his own newspapers, and each was suspicious of the other's sources.[3]

The enemy image leads to the application of a double standard of morality, which in turn reinforces the image because the enemy's motives are always presumed to be bad and those of our side are presumed to be good. The identical act is viewed as good if performed by our side and bad if performed by the enemy.

A psychologist showed some American fifth- and sixth-graders photographs of Russian roads lined with young trees. When he asked why the Russians had trees along the road, two answers were: "So that people won't be able to see what is going on beyond the road," and "It's to make work for the prisoners"; but when he asked why some American roads have trees planted along the side, the children said "for shade" or "to keep the dust down".[4]

The double standard of evaluation was illustrated by a formal study conducted in 1965 in which a large number of college freshmen were presented with 50 statements concerning belligerent and conciliatory actions that had been taken by both the United States and Russia. For half the students the acts were attributed to the United States, for the other half to the Soviet Union. They were asked to indicate their feelings about each statement by marking it from +3 (most favorable) to −3 (most unfavorable).

As might be expected, an action was scored more favorably when attributed to the United States than when attributed to Russia. For purposes of statistical analysis the scores were transformed into 0-to-6 scale, so that scores above 3 would be favorable and those below 3 unfavorable. For example, the average score for "the U.S. (Russia) has established rocket bases close to the borders of Russia (the U.S.)" was 4.7 for the United States version and 0.5 for the Russian one. "The U.S. (Russia) has stated that it was compelled to resume nuclear testing by the action of Russia (the U.S.)" was scored 4.2 in the United States form and 1.0 in the Russian one.[5]

The enemy image nations form of each other more or less corresponds to reality. Nations that failed to recognize that their enemies might be treacherous and warlike would not long survive. However, the enemy image impedes resolution of the conflict by causing both sides to overemphasize confirming information and filter out information that does not fit. It also leads contending nations each to acquire the evil characteristics attributed to the other. In combatting what is perceived to be the other's cruelty and treachery, each side itself becomes more cruel and treacherous.

The mutual enemy image is one example of how symbolic components aggravate human conflicts. Even more troublesome is the tendency to formulate domestic and international conflicts in philosophical terms rather than around tangible objectives. Blacks fight for better housing and better jobs, but these goals are subsumed under such concepts as freedom, equality and justice; whereas whites appeal to self-determination and law and order.

Domestic struggles may be bitter and destructive, but they do not seriously threaten the existence of the social system as long as both sides profess the same values. A society's life is at stake when one side challenges that society's basic assumption; as when blacks demand a separate state, which attacks the concept of integration of people of all races; or militant students of the New Left argue that the democratic system is no longer viable and must be overthrown.

International conflicts are caused by conflicts of national interests. As long as these interests are viewed primarily as tangible—such as control of territory, population or resources—and neither side strives for the complete occupation of the other, the conflicts remain within bounds. They become threatening to the survival of the contestants, and today to the survival of mankind, when the interests at stake are couched in terms of which "world view" shall prevail, and when the promulgator of each world view believes it cannot survive as long as the other exists.

Unfortunately, many persons today view international struggles in this way. They see all conflict as skirmishes in an apocalyptic struggle between Communism and Free Enterprise to determine which will eventually secure the allegiance of the whole world. Proponents of each ideology see the other as a never-ending threat that can be eliminated only by destruction of its advocates.

Conflicts over ideologies remove constraints on violence for two reasons. In contrast to fights over tangible aims, which stop when the aims are achieved, ideological struggles have no natural end. A fight over property ends when one side has firmly secured it, but an idea ceases to be a danger only with the death of the last survivor who holds it, and even then it may crop up again. Hence, religious wars tend to be especially bitter, stopping only when both sides are exhausted, with the survivors still clinging to their beliefs.

Ideologies often are more important sources of psychological security than possessions. Because of their ability to conceptualize, humans can come to recognize the insignificance of their own lives, which appear to be nothing more than brief, tiny, flashes of experience in a universe that does not seem to care. This idea is intolerable to many people, so to counteract it they create ideologies in order to give meaning to existence. For them, the loss of their ideology, as might follow defeat by a group that maintains an incompatible ideology, may be worse than biological death. So they prefer to die.

Traditionally, international wars were waged by the military of each side; that is, by institutions of a nation whose special function it was to defend or promote that nation's interests. The civilian populations were regarded as more or less innocent bystanders. They might get trampled under foot, to be sure, but they were not directly involved. In this way, international war differed from domestic strife. In the latter, the whole population is on the firing line.

Today, as a nation's military strength has come to include its civilian and industrial resources, as well as its army, and methods of killing have become more massive and indiscriminate, this distinction between international and domestic strife has largely broken down. A further reason for the blurring of this distinction is the rise of guerilla warfare as the main defense of weak nations against stronger ones that are attempting to subdue them. The success of guerillas depends on the active support of the civilian population.

In any case, international conflicts show a strong tendency to escalate. Once nations become engaged in war whatever inhibitions humans have against killing their own kind are abolished—and like other predators, we probably have some.

One reason for this is that so much of the killing is remote. If ordered to douse a child with burning napalm, even the most hardened soldier might hesitate a bit, but he can do it on a massive scale from an airplane. Mass methods of killing reduce the enemy to a statistic.

TV, which puts everyone on the firing line, reduces this impersonality, and so may have an inhibiting effect. Perhaps this is partly responsible for the unprecedented opposition to the war in Vietnam and decline in the sale of war toys.

An often overlooked facilitator of killing by humans is sheer obedience, which plays into the newer methods of mass killing. All social structure depends on a hierarchy of power, and members of even the most democratic societies readily obey legitimate authority. If they did not, social living would be impossible.

The power of obedience was elegantly, if somewhat horrifyingly, demonstrated by a study in which normal American adults were told by the experimenter that an experiment, for which they had volunteered, required them to deliver very painful, possibly lethal, shocks to an inoffensive stranger. About two-thirds of the subjects carried out these orders. The closer the subjects were to the victim psychologically, the more likely they were to disobey. But even when they had to hold the struggling, screaming victim's hand on the shock plate forcibly, about one third complied. (The victim, of course, was an accomplice. He received no shocks.) Perhaps most disquieting was the finding that if the subject only had to throw a master switch which enabled someone else to give the shock, over 90 per cent complied.[6]

It seems we are all too ready to delegate responsibility for our acts to a legitimate authority. It is not surprising that when a Polaris submarine commander was asked how he felt about the destructive power under his control, he replied: "I've never given it any thought. But, if we ever have to hit, we'll hit. And there won't be a second's hesitation."[7] The power of obedience to authority probably also explains in part why enemy soldiers slaughtered each other just as ruthlessly in hand-to-hand combat as with shells and bombs. But other factors also are undoubtedly involved.

Sheer self-defense is undoubtedly one factor and an additional one is the "dehumanization" of the enemy. One source of dehumanization already mentioned is the enemy's antipathetic ideology. He is no longer considered to be human, but becomes instead the embodiment of a hated abstraction, such as communism, imperialism, Islam. As a believer in false gods, he partakes of the demonic, and so he must be destroyed.

The enemy is *dehumanized* is another way by making him into a beast on the grounds that he commits atrocities. Denial that an enemy is human has proved an effective method of removing inhibitions to the slaughter of fellow humans. Whether a method of killing is viewed as an atrocity depends on whether it is considered legitimate, not on the amount of pain or suffering inflicted. Who can say whether it hurts more to be disemboweled than to be roasted to death by napalm? Yet in the Vietnam War, the United States regards the former as an atrocity while the National Liberation Front refers to napalm and crop poisoning as "the most cruel and barbaric means of annihilating people."[8] Each side continually invokes the atrocities of the other to arouse indignation and increase the urge to destroy the enemy.

Another powerful incentive to kill is associated with the preservation of self-image. Since the military man's self-esteem rests on his courage and willingness to die for his country, this aspect of his self-image is likely to become involved in his decision to fight. This creates a danger: if a conflict is sufficiently intense and prolonged, the primary objective of both antagonists may shift from the initial goals, to the goal of proving that one is more determined or more courageous than his enemy. The best way to do this is to be willing to keep fighting longer.

History is replete with examples. One is the Battle of Verdun, which cost the lives of nearly one million soldiers in World War I. According to a military historian, the battle continued long after its military significance had passed because: "it had somehow achieved a demonic existence of its own, far beyond the control of generals of either nation. Honor had become involved to an extent which made disengagement impossible." [9] Perhaps the state of mind of the generals—the soldiers, who did most of the dying had no choice but to obey orders—was analogous to that of persons who commit suicide rather than face intolerable loss of self-esteem.

The best hope of controlling group violence internationally lies in reducing the sense of frustration of the peoples of the underdeveloped world and strengthening their sense of community. This is a prerequisite for the development of effective international peacekeeping institutions.

It is a truism that anger is a major instigator of violence in humans and that frustration is a powerful source of anger. The important point is that the amount of frustration depends less on the amount of deprivation than on the size of the gap between what a person has and what he expects or believes he is entitled to have.

Recent urban riots cannot be explained by the low standard of living of the rioters. In absolute terms even the poorest dweller in the black ghetto is better off than millions of Asians. Yet the denizens of the Calcutta slums quietly starve to death, while the blacks in our cities explode with rage and frustration. Their bitterness derives from the difference between what they have and what they have been led to expect, and this gap has been increasing. The same phenomenon, which has been called "relative deprivation," explains the rising tide of violence in most of the world's newly independent countries. The citizens of these lands expected independence to bring a rise in the standard of living. Instead it often has been accompanied by a fall in living standards.

This sense of relative deprivation has been aggravated by television and especially by the transistor radio, which makes the poor of these nations aware as never before of what other people have. To overcome their frustration a rapid increase in their standard of living is required but, as with attempts to improve the lot of poor American blacks, aid to them must be offered in a way that preserves the self-respect of the recipients and permits them to share in decisions regarding their welfare.

This point was well stated by a black Vista worker: "Black people want black control of their lives and activities more than anything else. If they make mistakes, let them be black mistakes—we're tired of white mistakes in our lives."

Failure to observe this principle is largely the reason American economic aid has created more resentment than good will and why the Peace Corps, on the other hand, has been relatively successful.

The Peace Corps, as described by one of its senior psychological consultants, "must be seen as a program that is compellingly relevant to the recipients' well being, as a form of assistance that can be accepted without compromise of autonomy or loss of personal dignity." And to this end it operates on "revolutionary" principles: The volunteer lives simply, with the people . . . He is assigned to work under the supervision of host nationals within existing administrative structures."[10]

The Peace Corps' aid projects are defined as collaborative efforts, in which the volunteer learns from the host as well as teaches him. The goal is for the host to take over the job himself. The volunteer works as a peer among peers, not as a superior with inferiors. He uses the host's language and operates in general on the principle that other persons are more receptive to your views if you show that you understand and respect theirs.

Just as domestic tranquility in the United States depends on restoring a sense of community to all Americans, so world peace requires the creation of a sense of community of all the world's people, transcending their national allegiances. In the past, there was no prospect of achieving this goal, but now for the first time tremendous advances in electronic communications and mass transportation may be bringing it within reach. We have not, for example, even begun to use the potentialities of international communication satellites to increase international understanding.

With potential enemies, these means offer new opportunities for constant communication without the distorting effects of intermediaries, such as the hot line, and for direct surveillance by satellites. Both of these methods should yield more accurate information as to the opponents' intentions and capabilities. In itself, this would impose restraints on preparations for hostilities by both sides, and would also help to reduce any distortions of the enemy image.

Public opinion is an important inhibitor of violence within communities. One can discern the beginnings of a world opinion whose increased power can perhaps be seen in the striking differences between Russia's behavior toward Czechoslovakia in 1968, and its attack on Hungary a decade ago. Russia's motives are probably the same, but the violent subjugation of Czechoslovakia is not easy to achieve with the whole world, and especially the other Communist parties, looking on.

More importantly, nations whose interests conflict also have many interests in common. These are jeopardized by an intensification of hostility, and common interests loom increasingly large as the world shrinks and opportunities for fruitful international cooperation increase. Today the U.S. and the U.S.S.R. have a strong, short-term common interest in preventing the spread of nuclear weapons to non-nuclear powers. They also have a long-range common interest in promoting international stability, because local flareups always carry the potential of forcing a major confrontation. Thus at this writing, although the United States and the Soviets back opposing sides, both are working to maintain the Israeli-Egyptian cease fire. This common concern also creates incentives for joint undertakings to raise the economic level of the impoverished nations.

Social psychologists have shown that the most powerful antidote to enmity between groups is cooperation toward a goal that both groups want but that neither can achieve alone. At first glance survival would seem to be such a goal, because all people desire it and its achievement requires international cooperation. Under some circumstances, however, survival takes a back seat to the urge to destroy the enemy. Moreover, the long-term measures required for national survival, such as general disarmament, appear to increase the short-term risks of destruction by an enemy, so that mobilizing the urge to survive works both ways.

Modern science has created many opportunities for cooperative activities among nations to attain goals that all of them want but none can achieve alone. We know from the experience of one such activity, the International Geophysical Year, which led to the treaty demilitarizing the Antarctic, that attitudes of cooperation can be fostered and gradually become embodied in institutions. Scientists have devised dozens of such projects which can be activated as soon as the world's leaders are willing. The most hopeful of these may be projects to control environmental pollution, since it increasingly threatens people of all nations and can be achieved only by international cooperation, nor does cooperation to this end involve any risk.

In addition to building attitudes of cooperation, some of these activities provide constructive outlets for man's aggressive competitiveness, which must be rechanneled if it is not to be released periodically in war. The conquests of outer space and of the undersea world meet this need because they demand the fullest exercise of courage, determination, and all the other manly virtues. And they are highly competitive. At the same time, people everywhere look upon these ventures as projects of all nations, not the monopoly of any one nation. Thus, both Americans and Russians can sincerely mourn when an astronaut or a cosmonaut is lost, and they can sincerely congratulate one another on a new space triumph, but they could hardly be mutually congratulatory on the invention of an improved nuclear missile.

A sense of community among peoples of different nations would lay the essential groundwork for the creation on an international scale of a domestic model for controlling aggression; namely the rule of law administered by specialized institutions.

The job of devising these new international institutions with machinery for enforcing their decisions under international law is primarily one for political scientists and jurists. Psychiatrists and psychologists must guard against delusions of grandeur in this regard. Their contribution at best represents no more than 10 per cent of the solution. But it is a crucial 10 per cent. Sociopsychological analyses *can* make significant contributions. They can identify the psychological factors that intensify the image of the enemy and aggravate armed conflict, as the first step toward effectively combatting these factors. They can also suggest how certain psychological principles might be mobilized to foster the feeling of world community upon which the new international institutions must rely for acceptance. Perhaps these contributions, when they are integrated with the more important ones from other disciplines, may yet be enough to tip the balance in favor of survival.

REFERENCES

1. Gallup Poll: "Image" of Red Powers, *Santa Barbara News-Press*, 1966.
2. Angell, R.C., Dunham, V.S., and Singer, J.D.: J Confl Resolu 8:329, 1964.
3. Krauskopf, K.: Science 134:539, 1961.
4. Bronfenbrenner, U.: Why Do Russians Plant Trees Along the Road, *Saturday Review*, 1963.
5. Oskamp, S.: Psychol Rep 16:43, 1965.
6. Milgram, S.: Int J Psychiat 6:259, 1968.
7. Cary, W.H., Jr.: *Madmen at Work, the Polaris Story*, Philadelphia: The American Friends Service Committee.
8. Malinowsky, R.V.: *The New York Times*, 1966.
9. Horne, A.: Verdun—The Reason Why, *The New York Times Magazine*, 1966.
10. Hobbs, N.: Amer Psychol 18:47, 1963.

CORRECTIONS IN A DEMOCRATIC SOCIETY

S. L. Halleck, M.D.

A democratic society should respond to illegal behavior effectively and humanely. American society fails to do this. Our current system of crime control is notoriously inefficient. It is a system dominated by inequities and blatant oppressions which are not consistent with the values or needs of a humane society.

There was a time when I believed in the virtues of our crime control system. My first intensive contact with prisoners began after my medical internship when, as a member of the U. S. Public Health Service, I was assigned to the Medical Center for Federal Prisoners. I soon learned that prisons were frightening places and that prisoners were frightening men.

In my attempts to reduce my own anxiety I identified with the agents of punishment and learned to view the criminal as a lesser being. The custodial staff seemed reasonably enlightened and, given my conventional attitudes towards crime, it did not seem to me that prisoners were being treated too badly. I hardly noticed that black and white prisoners were segregated, and that prisoners were given no opportunity to behave like normal human beings.

It was not long until I realized that I could do little to help the criminal. I returned to the university a disillusioned but wiser man. I know today that neither messianic zeal nor administrative skill will reform the system. I also know more certainly than ever that the system is wrong. My work with students, my life in the free atmosphere of the university and, hopefully, maturity have persuaded me that the criminal's behavior is an understandable and distinctly human behavior and that treating criminals inhumanely only makes them behave like animals.

Dr. Halleck is professor of psychiatry at the University of Wisconsin Medical School, Madison. This paper was originally presented to the Center for the Study of Democratic Institutions in August of 1968, and parts of it reprinted in the CENTER Magazine; this is the first publication of the paper in its entirety.

I also am convinced that changes in our correctional system should not be minor, but radical. The attempts by liberal reformers to compromise and work within the system have been ineffective. Reform must begin at the beginning, with a clear definition of the basic needs and values of a democratic society which must control crime. And nothing will change unless we uncompromisingly expose and reject those elements in the current system which are antagonistic to our basic needs and values.

Protection

Those values which should guide a free society in its efforts to control crime are best described under the heading of *protection*. There must first of all be protection of those who are in danger of being injured by a criminal act. The rights, the property and the person of the law-abiding citizen must be safeguarded. At the same time, the rights of the offender or criminal also must be protected. One goal of any humane and compassionate society is to keep as many citizens as possible as free as possible. A community that is committed to a belief in the worth of each individual cannot banish a citizen, disenfranchise him, or cage him without hurting itself.

The value of punishment in a democratic society is limited. Perhaps society has the right to inflict pain upon those who offend against it. But this does not mean that punishment itself can be a guiding value in a correctional system. Rather, punishment is of value primarily as it serves the goal of protecting society and its institutions.

Assuming the dominance of the value of protection, what are the specific needs of a democratic society in dealing with crime?

First, there is a need for rapid apprehension and public designation of those who have attempted to harm the community. The society needs to know who is attacking it, how it is being attacked, and the reasons why it is being attacked. The potential offender needs to know that his actions have offended the community and that the community is concerned about his behavior. The apprehended criminal needs to know this also.

Second, the community must decide the extent of its concern and what, if any, protective measures it must take in its own interest. The decision-making process must deal with three types of action, each of which has different implications for the freedom of the offender.

At the first level, the community might wish to decide that no action other than public acknowledgement of community disapproval is necessary. Or it might offer some form of assistance such as education or counseling which would help to deal with the offender's problems and decrease the likelihood of his committing another offense.

Where the crime is more serious, or where the possibility of repetition is great, the community might have to restrict some of the offender's freedoms. In the interest of the offender's victims, it might, for example, force him to make restitution for property loss. Or, in the interest of protecting the community from further offenses, it might order the offender to seek the help of professional counselors or present himself for regular surveillance by designated agents of social control.

Finally, the community might decide that it cannot be protected unless the offender's right to move about freely is gravely restricted. In such cases it must define the need for restriction, the conditions of restriction, and the circumstances under which restriction can be terminated.

A third need of the democratic society is to educate and reform those who must be restricted so that they can rejoin the community as soon as possible. The system which deals with this task must be flexible. It must allow for early restoration of rights to those who make rapid progress in coming to terms with the problems that have created their antisocial acts. At the same time, it must provide for continued restriction of those who remain a threat to the community. Finally, it must be concerned that the rehabilitation process does not proceed at the expense of the offender's essential humanness. Ideally, the criminal should return to a free society as a more effective, socially conscious and responsible citizen.

Punishment

While I have rejected the importance of punishment as a primary value in controlling crime, there is still the question of whether deliberate punishment of offenders is, in any sense, a need of a democratic society. It might be argued that this question is academic because irrespective of society's motives, the offender will experience any deprivation of freedom as punishment. Practically, however, there is an important difference between a society which restricts offenders vindictively and a society which restricts without motives of revenge. The vengeful society is likely to impose longer sentences under crueler conditions. It is also likely to create a greater gap between the designated offender and the mass of law-abiding citizens.

There are three major arguments for deliberately punishing offenders. First, punishment serves society's need for vengeance or retaliation. Second, punishment serves as a deterrent to crime. Third, punishment has a rehabilitative effect upon the offender.

The first argument is the weakest. Some individuals believe that society's punishment of the criminal has a cleansing effect upon the entire community, that the discharge of the community's aggression towards a wrongdoer helps to "stabilize" all citizens, individually and collectively. By punishing the criminal, society finds an outlet for its aggressions and at the same time emphasizes the virtue of its conforming citizens. This argument is vague and unproved. The quality of "stability" based on vindictiveness is questionable. And it is not unlikely that society's release of aggression against the offender creates a social climate of antagonism in which those who have grievances against society become progressively more alienated and aggressive.

While most citizens hold strong views on the value of punishment as a deterrent, there is no scientific way to evaluate its usefulness. Those who argue against punishment often point out that American society has one of the harshest systems of punishment and at the same time a sky-rocketing crime rate. The implication is that punishment has failed to deter crime. Obviously, this is not a scientific conclusion, because it could just as logically be argued that punishment in America is not really harsh enough to deter crime. We can only approach the question of punishment as a deterrent by examining the way similar groups of people behave under different punitive systems and by speculating as to the reasons for their behavior.

The evidence is far from conclusive. Those states which invoke the harshest penalty—death—for the crime of murder have as many or more murders than states with lesser penalties. States with liberal parole systems do not have higher crime rates than those which impose sterner restrictions. This would suggest that punishment does not deter.

On the other hand, it is true that fewer individuals will risk speeding or driving an automobile when intoxicated if they know that the penalties for such offenses are severe. Threats of punishment are part of child-rearing in every culture and it is likely that fear of some type of community punishment or penalty is a potent force in keeping most of us law-abiding most of the time.

One way of explaining the contradictory evidence is to hypothesize that a favorable response to punishment depends upon the nationality, maturity and social involvement of the individual. To the extent that one is immature, irrational, or not committed to the system, he will be less likely to be deterred by threats. This would explain the failure of our system of punishment to deter crime, because there is ample evidence that most offenders are immature, behave irrationally and feel alienated from society.

It also is true that for most persons punishment is not a meaningful deterrent unless there also is a strong possibility of being apprehended. Thousands of young people smoke marihuana and thousands more sell it. If convicted of possessing marihuana a person could spend up to 10 years in prison. As a convicted seller he might face life imprisonment. Youth continues to violate the marihuana statutes because they know that even if punishment is potentially severe, the possibilities of apprehension and conviction for marihuana usage are extremely remote. Many other crimes which carry severe penalties, but which have a high prevalance because of difficulty in enforcement, could be listed.

To the extent that apprehension of offenders and designation of criminality is efficient, the degree of harshness of punishment becomes less relevant to the question of deterrence. A major need of a democratic society is for an efficient system of identifying offenders. If this could be accomplished, the humiliation of being publically designated as a criminal might be the only deterrent needed for most crimes. Only the most severe offenses would require punitive measures and in most cases the fear of the restriction which might be imposed for society's protection would be a sufficient deterrent.

The value of punishment in reforming and rehabilitating offenders is even more questionable than its value in deterring crime. This does not mean that punishment cannot alter behavior. If painful or aversive stimuli are regularly applied to an individual immediately after he has committed a particular act, the recurrence of that act usually becomes more unlikely. In such a learning process, however, it is critical that the painful stimulus immediately follow the behavior one wants to eliminate so that the behavior and the punishment can be inter-related. There is at present no practical way of applying such punishment to offenders. The current practice of sentencing men to imprisonment for months or years after the criminal act has taken place is not an effective means of teaching restraint. It embitters, but it does not reform.

Although punishment is futile, as a rule, and a harmful waste of our human resources, there is still one important area in which punishment might be necessary in a democratic society, and that is in the area of social protest.

Most criminal acts can be viewed as responses to real or imagined oppression. In American society oppression of certain minority groups is real. One way of looking at crime is to see it as an attempt to relieve oppression as a kind of social activism or dissent. By violating the law, an offender is often directly or indirectly clamoring for social change. The boundaries between protest and crime are becoming less clear in modern society. Those who protest the war and oppression of minority groups must often break the law to make their point. Much of what appears to be selfish crime, such as rioting and looting, is also having an increasing influence in bringing about social change. Lawless rioting in our cities has probably had more influence in helping the poor and the blacks than have most lawful pleas or demands for change.

Crime is one index of imperfection in a society which sometimes calls for changes in the community as a whole rather than for changes in the offender. If society insisted upon reforming every offender it could negate the protest value of crime caused by social oppression. The offender whose criminality consists of a response to social oppression has a right to have his protest taken seriously. In a sense he has a right to a dignified and honorable punishment. This is a borderline area.

Having considered the needs of a democratic society in its efforts to control crime, it is possible to examine the degree to which the American system for the administration of correctional justice meets these needs. My remarks will be concerned primarily with the impact of the system upon offenders who are uninterested in, or unaware of, the protest value of their criminality. As major weaknesses are described, I will suggest means by which our system could be changed so that it might actually serve the needs of a democratic community.

The Apprehension of Offenders and Designation of Criminality

Our police are unable to protect our citizens adequately. This inability results not only because there are too many criminals and too few police. Nor is it simply a matter of poor training. The American police officer is prevented from becoming an effective agent of protection by his task orientation and overall world view. A major part of the policeman's job requires him to try to enforce laws that are, for the most part, unenforceable. Police officers spend an incredible number of hours investigating "crimes without victims," crimes such as drug abuse, gambling, homosexuality and prostitution. None of these "criminal" behaviors can be controlled effectively in a democratic society. The police officer is put into the frustrating position of imposing conformity upon deviant groups who are skilled in resisting conformity. Thrust into the role of arbiter of community values, he comes to see himself as a force against evil rather than as a force for protecting society. To the extent that he becomes preoccupied with social deviance rather than with serious crime, he becomes a person who is suspicious of all minority groups and a potent agent of the status quo.

Many police officers believe that use of marijuana inevitably leads to drug addiction and other criminal activities. Many are convinced that all homosexuals, exhibitionists and voyeurs are likely to commit assaultive sex crimes. While they are correct in viewing activities such as drug abuse, gambling and prostitution as being a source of profit for organized crime, they forget that it is only our society's stringent definitions of evil which allows organized crime to reap so much profit from man's frailties.

To the extent that our society has used police officers to control alleged evil, it has neglected its obligation to develop scientific methods for preventing and detecting serious crime. The great majority of major crimes are never solved. The odds favor the criminal. Armed robbers are rarely caught. Rape or murder of random victims is practically unsolvable unless the offender is caught in the act or confesses. We allow our citizens such easy access to weapons of destruction that murder of friends, family and innocent bystanders has become an everyday phenomenon.

In a judicial system governed by the philosophy of punishment there is an insidious preoccupation with the protocols of justice and vengeance which ultimately harrasses the police officer. Even when an officer does a superb job of apprehending an offender the arrest will not often result in judicial action. Our elaborate judicial procedures protect citizens from unjust punishment, but at the same time they allow many offenders to be released without any public designation of their guilt. The dedicated police officer soon finds that his best efforts go unrewarded. Those he apprehends, particularly if they are white, wealthy or wise, are not likely to be found guilty. He soon becomes cynical and convinced that he is the only decent force in a corrupt system. He may either become corrupt himself, or he may come to see himself as an "avenging angel" of justice, one who is entitled to rise above the system and to enforce morality in a manner that satisfies his own prejudices.

Reform of our system for apprehending criminals would require radical changes in the structure of society. A major step would be to stop defining drug abuse, gambling and certain forms of sexual behavior as crimes, to see them as self-destructive acts which would best be controlled—if they need to be controlled—through education and counseling. It is ridiculous to invest so much police time in the endless and usually unsuccessful task of ferreting out marihuana smokers, "numbers" players or homosexuals. If our police were freed of this onerous task, they could devote their attention to more dangerous criminals.

It is becoming almost trite to insist that the standards for education and compensation of police officers be improved. Unfortunately, most such proposals do not go far enough. Those who are entrusted with maintaining the public order should be among the most esteemed of the community's citizens. The policeman does more counseling than a social worker, makes more crucial decisions than a judge and takes more risks than a soldier. It is not unrealistic to demand that police officers obtain a college education, and it is only good sense to insist that they be compensated as adequately as a judge or a social worker.

Our clumsy judicial processes plague the community as a whole even more than they do the police officer. Trial delays force many who have never been convicted of a crime to spend months in jails. Our bail system discriminates against the poor who are not only jailed while awaiting trial but who must then plead their cases from the disadvantaged position of having already been a prisoner. Because of our demands for punishment we have rightfully provided that conviction can take place only if proof of a crime is beyond reasonable doubt and if a large number of technical conditions are met. The man who can afford the best lawyer, and who can be free on bail to assist in the preparation of his case, has a distinct edge over the disadvantaged offender. There is neither efficiency nor justice in this system. We punish the poor, the black and the uninformed, but we allow a discouragingly large number of offenders to go unpunished.

An efficient system for designating criminality would require trial without undue delay and equal access of all social classes to bail and competent legal assistance. Even more important it would require a social climate in which more offenders would be willing to acknowledge their misdeeds. Such a climate would be possible only if our society were more concerned with *protection* than with punishment.

Our current system assumes the existence of a "criminal class", committed to a predatory life and forever at war with society. This assumption becomes a self-fulfilling prophecy once the offender is convinced that society is at war with him. The great majority of apprehended offenders do not begin their criminal careers because they are deliberately anti-social, but because they are desperate or exposed to intolerable social circumstances. Most would be willing to admit their guilt if they could be convinced that the resulting community action would hold out some possibility of helping them find a decent role in society.

The System of Community Protection

Although our society is inept in apprehending and convicting offenders, its treatment of those it does find guilty of having committed a criminal act is even more inefficient and irrational. Again, it is our adherence to the misuse of punishment which precludes a rational system of community protection.

The decision as to what is to be done with the convicted offender is left to a single judge or jury, individuals who may have too little training or too little interest in the process of rehabilitation. Only a few courts have access to psychological or social studies of the offender at the time of sentencing. Whatever information happens to be available is limited in usefulness by the limited options of the sentencing agency. The court can suspend sentencing, which it rarely does; impose fines; recommend probation; or recommend imprisonment.

The uses of fines and probation is limited by community vindictiveness and the resources of the offender. There has been no serious effort to develop a system of penalties which would force the offender to make some sort of restitution to his victims. The ordinary convicted offender is sent to prison. He is removed from the community and is jailed in institutions notoriously deficient in providing the education, training and counseling that are crucial to rehabilitation.

In most jurisdictions when the court recommends imprisonment it must impose a relatively fixed sentence. The use of parole helps to modify the rigidity of this practice only slightly. Fixed sentencing is not consistent with the goal of community protection. If we believe that a man should be incarcerated only until he is ready to take his place in the community, fixed sentencing must be viewed as a practice which hurts the community. It requires continued punishment of those who may already have been rehabilitated and thereby wastes community resources. But, if we desire to protect society from assaultive criminals, we cannot assume that all offenders will be fully rehabilitated when their fixed sentence has expired. Many offenders "do their time" and emerge from prison as dangerous or even more dangerous than they were before.

It is generally assumed that only the most anti-social, the most dangerous and the most recalcitrant offenders reach our penitentiaries. Yet our prisons are swarming with check forgers, car thieves, burglars, non-assaultive sex offenders and, in some states, a discouragingly large number of men who have failed to meet alimony payments. While these men have shorter sentences than rapists, armed robbers and murderers, they are subject to the same kinds of punishment and treatment as the more dangerous criminals. Our system of sentencing seems to imply that protection of property is as important as protection of people. By failing to discriminate in our treatment of assaultive versus non-assaultive offenders we overpunish minor offenders and at the same time fail to protect the community from dangerous offenders.

It would seem that in an area as complex as deciding disposition and treatment of convicted offenders, psychiatrists and other behavioral scientists would be asked to play a major role. This is rarely the case. Instead, the healing professions are asked to play a tangential role in our legal processes, that of attempting to designate a few individuals (usually those who are well off financially or those who have committed sensational crimes) as too sick to be punished.

By relating the philosophical concept of responsibility to the metaphorical concept of mental illness, psychiatrists manage to "bootleg" a little compassion for a few offenders and the courts are eager to have them do so. Except for the occasional benefits received by one who is labelled "sick" instead of "bad," however, this practice does little to serve the needs of society. It is a liberal solution which ultimately makes things worse.

By seeking exceptions to the punishment process for a few, psychiatrists indirectly condone the current system and perpetuate it by camouflaging its most blatant weaknesses. If society chose to punish mentally ill offenders it would also have to face up to the cruelty of punishing other offenders who are equally deserving of our compassion. Humane treatment of the few enables the system to justify continued oppression of the many.

Our system for protecting society from those already designated as criminals could be revitalized by measures which are both practical and humane. The first need is to make wider use of judicial options that do not require incarceration. Certainly some offenders have to be locked up, for it is clear that they will offend again until something is done to change them. Yet, too many offenders are locked up unnecessarily. Many offenders can be reformed by a simple warning, by finding them a job, by education or by counseling. Most offenders against property rights could be handled better by requiring them to work to compensate their victims rather than by sending them off to a distant prison. Recent studies indicate that fewer than 15 per cent of first time sex offenders commit a new offense whether they are incarcerated or not. This means that many of them are being needlessly confined in prisons.

A second need is for indeterminate sentencing. Most offenders should be returned to society as soon as they are rehabilitated. Dangerous offenders should be confined until they can be safely released.

Our greatest need is in the area of understanding dangerous behavior. We must learn to determine which offenders are dangerous to society, and we must discover methods for treating them. Assisting society in this task would seem to be a natural function of psychiatry and the social sciences. If the amount of professional energy invested in determination of criminal responsibility were rechanneled into the study of dangerous behavior, psychiatrists might yet make a real contribution to criminology.

Rehabilitation of Criminals

There are some individuals who are so likely to commit assaultive crimes or repeated crimes against property that they must be physically confined. In American society this usually means confinement to a walled institution which is separated from the rest of the community. Those who must suffer incarceration are likely to be members of minority groups, the poor, the black, and the uneducated.

Every society must at times restrain some of its citizens. Our society elects to return the overwhelming majority of offenders to the community. Logically this means that society needs to reform or rehabilitate those offenders whom it incarcerates. Reform, therefore, is not an idealistic goal but a vital necessity. But our society wishes not only to reform, it also wishes to punish.

I will not dwell on the barbarisms of American prisons which I and other writers have described in detail. Instead, I will attempt to describe what kinds of measures would be useful in helping offenders return to society, and will comment upon how a rational system of corrections might implement such measures. It will become clear that the goals of punishment have completely dominated and ruled out the possibility of rational reformation. Our prisons do not turn out better citizens. They release men who are more likely to behave like untamed animals or passive robots.

One of the major requirements for being a good citizen in a democratic society is to have the capacity to assume responsibility for one's own actions. The mature citizen realizes that when he acts, certain consequences will follow, and that he is at least in part accountable for these consequences. The passive citizen believes that he has no choice, that his actions are dictated by others and that he cannot be held responsible for what he does. The correctional process must begin by teaching the offender to take responsibility for his behavior.

Prisons, by enforcing passivity among inmates, fail to teach responsibility. The offender is totally dependent upon others for his food, his clothing and his recreation. Conditions of prison life are structured so as to limit life situations which require choice.

There is no sound reason for not allowing prison inmates to structure their own lives, even within the confines of the prison. Inmates need to live in a world in which their actions have consequences. This means that they must have some opportunity to earn, rather than to be given, the necessities of existence. Prisoners should be granted the opportunity to do meaningful work, and the opportunity to be realistically compensated for that work. Prisoners also need a certain amount of power; authority to govern themselves within the institution, to elect officers from their own leaders, to arbitrate with prison administrators, and to participate in decisions concerning their own future. All of these steps may seem unrealistic at first glance, but such measures have been utilized in a few experimental programs with notable results.

Another way of thinking about responsibility is in terms of being responsible to others. Every citizen has some responsibility to try to support himself and his family and some responsibility to be an active participant in the political process. Most of those who reach prison are amazingly deficient at work skills. Many lack economic skills, such as budget keeping, which are essential for survival in a technological society. They know practically nothing about the use of group power, moral power, or the opportunities for legally sanctioned activism. Prisons should teach these skills, but they do not. Feeble attempts are made to teach economic responsibility, but political responsibility is actively discouraged.

It is time to re-examine the practice of denying convicted offenders the right to vote. Simply because a man has used poor judgment in one area of life does not mean his total judgment is so impaired that the community should be deprived of his political voice. If prisoners could vote it would be difficult for the rest of society to ignore them. Once the public paid attention to criminals it might be stimulated to do something about their plight. But this is not the primary reason for giving prisoners the right to vote. When one participates in a political process, he becomes less alienated and more responsible to the system.

In this regard, it is interesting to note that many criminals who have become involved in legal activism on their own behalf seem to change their attitudes and behavior. When an offender gains his freedom by appealing to the courts under one of the newer Supreme Court rulings he learns that all is not hopeless, that he can be responsible for what happens to him. Often this is enough to make him a law-abiding citizen. It is likely that participation in the political process would have the same effect.

If the reformed criminal is to take his place as a useful member of society, he must come to see himself as more than a faceless being. He is unlikely to develop a firm sense of identity and initiative unless he has an opportunity to live in a community that is small enough to grant him a distinct and important place in its functionings. The social and psychological data we have about treatment in institutions indicates that good results are inversely related to the size of the institution. Yet, treatment of criminals in American society is conducted in huge overcrowded institutions which are depersonalizing and dehumanizing. Ideally, institutions should house approximately 50, at the most 200, inmates. Prisons in America house thousands of inmates, and they are growing larger.

Much of the deprivation and conflict which leads to criminal behavior is generated within the family. A reformed offender must learn to live with his family comfortably and effectively. This would logically suggest that the rehabilitation process should take place in as close proximity to the family unit as possible. Ideally, parents and wives should be available for counseling and family therapy. This can best be accomplished when inmates are housed close to their communities and when there are ample funds and space available for regular family visits. Or it could be implemented by making greater use of furloughs for prisoners. Our current system is blind to these possibilities. Part of the punishment process consists of separating a prisoner from his family. Visits are rare and are conducted under the rigid scrutiny of prison guards. Furloughs or trial visits are even rarer. Family counseling is almost non-existent.

Much of the conflict leading to criminal behavior is generated by the community as well as the family. It is necessary to include community agencies in the rehabilitation process. This is especially important at the time of release when the offender is faced with the painful task of re-entering what has often become a strange world. All of this would most easily be accomplished if the offender were incarcerated as close to the community as possible and had as many opportunities to visit the community as possible. Again the American prison system does exactly the opposite. It isolates the offender from his community and sees to it that his return to it is so abrupt as to be a severe stress in itself.

A defective capacity to relate to women is at the root of many sex offenders and a large number of other crimes. One of the tasks of reformation for at least some offenders is to learn how to seek and find intimacy with a member of the opposite sex. Ideally, men and women should have an opportunity to come together within our institutions in everyday social situations and possibly in group counseling sessions. In the American penal system men are not allowed to mingle with women under any circumstances. Few women are employed in prisons and those that do get inside are selected primarily for their remoteness and their spinsterly qualities.

Those offenders who are imprisoned are usually deficient in education and work skills. At the very least the prison experience should provide enough education and vocational training to give them a fair opportunity to compete for jobs. Ideally, given the deprivations which most offenders have experienced, reformation should go even farther and provide the prisoner with exceptional training.

If the prisoner, upon release, had acquired specialized skill in a field such as computer programming, electronics or social service, he might have a chance to overcome his hardships. Again, our system does the wrong thing. It provides only token educational opportunities. It offers dreary and meaningless work only as a substitute for total inactivity. Making license plates or working in a jute mill does not prepare an offender for life in a technological society.

Prison officials often maintain that limiting work opportunities is practical insofar as most offenders would not be able to find good jobs even if they had adequate skills. This leads to practices such as putting blacks to work in the laundry and bakery, on the ground that these will be the only kind of job opportunities open to them in the community. This is another instance where assumptions become self-fulfilling prophecies.

Finally, the rehabilitation process must convince the offender that there is hope in the outside world, and that life can be better than it was before he was incarcerated. The offender must come to know that there are people who care about his plight and that such individuals have the power to do something to help him. It is in this area that the punishment process exerts its most malignant influence. No man can leave an American prison with as much trust of the world as he had when he came in. Few learn to hope. Few experience the kind of love and concern from their fellow man which makes life seem worthwhile. Our prisons must be changed so that they attract compassionate people who have the interest and the will to reach out to prison inmates and help them find rewarding lives.

Changing the System
Hardly anything I have said is new. Some of my suggestions may be provocative. Most of them, however, have been accepted for decades by knowledgeable and concerned persons. Yet, little happens. In an age of revolution, when every variety of arbitrary institution or value is being challenged, our system of correctional justice remains unchallenged.

Recent Supreme Court decisions which are directed towards protecting the offender's legal rights have been hailed as major reforms in the system. It is true that these decisions have encouraged many to begin to familiarize themselves with the plight of the criminal, and this may have long-term benefits. The immediate advantages of the Supreme Court decisions, however, are more illusory than real. Protecting the rights of offenders does add more justice to the punishment process. But it also strengthens the process by ameliorating its weaknesses.

The Supreme Court and the legal profession have not changed the system. Who then will change the system? Certainly not its victims. Offenders are too powerless, too oppressed and usually too inept to fight their own cause. Giving offenders the right to vote would help, but such a development is not imminent.

It is also unlikely that change will be initiated by those who now run the system. Once one begins to work in a correctional setting he develops certain attitudinal sets of psychological defenses which make it difficult for him to see the human problems of the offender. Criminals are not pleasant people to deal with, and in the correctional setting they often become vicious. The average correctional worker learns to deal with them by seeing them as subhuman or "humanoid". He anticipates their perversity and aggressiveness, and the inmates satisfy his expectations by acting perverse and aggressive. While correctional workers begin their job with benign and humanistic motivations, it is a rare worker who maintains this attitude for very long. It is an even rarer worker who can step back from a situation and think creatively about reformation or change.

It might be hoped that revolutionaries would attack the correctional system, just as they have been attacking other institutions in our society. When it comes to crime however, radicals are strangely silent. The New Left, in its passionate outcries for the whole of humanity seems oblivious to the suffering of its next door neighbors. Older revolutionaries are not much interested in reforming a system which not only brings out the worst in a society they wish to destroy but which sometimes also provides recruits for the revolutionary process.

Rightwing extremists who continually espouse the cause of freedom have little compunction in taking freedom away from those who are guilty of the least affront against society. Strangely enough the most useful reform in the correctional area has come from individual citizens of rather conservative nature. But they have been few in number and their voices have been small.

Reform will come about only when we Americans decide to learn something about crime; when we are willing to give up our unfounded notions about crime and violence and view the criminal as a human being who is not too unlike ourselves. It is a rare American who ever visits a police station, a court or a prison. Most college students never do; very few law students do. If there is any hope of major reform it rests in the possibility and our increasing concern with crime will encourage us to learn about the human problems of crime and corrections. Education is the one factor that may eventually allow Americans to say, "This system is wrong; it is unjustifiable; it must change".

A Concluding Note

In "Psychiatry and Dilemmas of Crime," I argued that crime could be considered one of several adaptations to social oppression and the feeling of helplessness which is generated by such oppression. Crime is most likely to occur when oppression is great and when the opportunities to seek other adaptations such as conformity, mental illness, or socially approved activism are limited.

This highly over-simplified scheme suggests several approaches towards reducing crime. Two of these approaches recently have become rallying cries for advocates of differing political viewpoints. Some argue that we can reduce crime by attacking its source, by doing away with oppressions in the lives of our citizens. Others believe that we can decrease the attraction of the criminal adaptation by harshly punishing the criminal.

In an age of affluence and relative freedom, the advocates of reducing oppression have a hard time making their case. Americans do seem, at least superficially, to be less oppressed than any group in the world at this time or at any time in history. Why should so many be willing to break the law? The answer can be found only by recognizing the psychological needs of man in a changing world. The rise of technology and the ever increasing rate of change in the conditions of everyday existence in the post war world have radically altered our perspectives.

We are now driven to live in the present. The future is too uncertain and sometimes too bleak to sit back quietly and wait. People want things now and are unwilling to put up with oppressions they may have tolerated in past decades. (Stated somewhat whimsically, "If people feel they are sailing on the SS Titanic, they want to go first class.")

It is also true that the knowledge explosion and the impact of the communications media have made it easier for people to perceive oppressions in their lives. It is no longer possible to deceive people into accepting conforming adaptations through hypocrisy, dogma or institutionalized values. Everyone is more aware of subtle oppressions in their lives, and fewer and fewer citizens are willing to tolerate them.

Faced with the problem of a restive citizenry, those in authority are tempted to control crime by suppressing it. The demands to "get tough" with the criminal sound louder every day.

Although I have spoken against punishment, it must be admitted that given certain stipulations, punishment might be quite effective in facilitating social stability and control. If our society does not care about rehabilitating deviant citizens, if it does not care what it does to people and if it is willing to be violent itself, then it is conceivable that punishment might be very effective indeed. It is a far simpler solution than trying to understand or respond to the grievances of oppressed minorities.

The behavioral scientist can do no more than describe the psychological results of alternate correctional methods. Ultimately, the manner in which a society chooses to control crime depends upon its political goals. If we value conformity, authoritarianism and preservation of the status quo, there is no need to observe any limits in our efforts to supress the criminal. If we value tolerance, freedom and change, our task is more difficult. We then must find a way of bringing the criminal back into the community and at the same time correct those inequities in the community which generated his criminality.

WHAT IS THE CAUSE OF VIOLENCE?

Roy R. Grinker, Sr., M.D.

What is *the* cause of current human violence?

We can make at least one generalization. Aggression and/or violence is *not* a simple, unitary, monolithic phenomenon. Although aggression, violence, hostility and revolution are loosely defined terms that suggest unitary concepts, we should resist responding to questions of non-professionals and the news media such as "what is *the* cause of violence?"

Acts of violence may seem to stem from a single cause, or a single historical trend. Their explosiveness often gives this impression. I believe, however, that a systems flow chart covering many social events over the past decade would reveal a confluence of multiple causes of violence, where several factors come together at approximately the same time and exceed the threshold of suppression through mutual reinforcement.

It was not so long ago that we despaired of the future of our youth who seemed apathetic. Then their uniforms of dirty white saddle shoes, khaki-slacks and T-shirts identified the gold-fish swallowers and the telephone booth packers. Today we are faced with angry vocal activists who demand, destroy, and accept no compromises whether the issue be the war, the draft, the civil rights, black power, or the students' revolt.

If we maintain our own "cool" and view these issues as objectively as possible, we must recognize they are important, and basically need action. Even most of us over 30 years of age believe that wars should be stopped, that blacks' freedom is long overdue, and that our educational system is stagnant and antiquated and has steadily deteriorated.

Yet *we* have been the apathetic ones who believed that slow evolutionary processes would inevitably result in desirable changes. But changes have not

Dr. Grinker is director of the Institute for Psychosomatic and Psychiatric Research and Training, Chicago; chairman of the Department of Psychiatry, Michael Reese Hospital and Medical Center, Chicago, and professor of psychiatry at the Pritzker School of Medicine, University of Chicago.

occurred or, if so, in such slight amounts that they are barely noticeable. The significant changes which have occurred in civil rights have only encouraged the blacks' demand for more and faster changes.

Yet this is not the whole story, because individual crimes of violence are increasing, children are acting-out violence in play, violence in general is given instant exposure on T.V., and high-school students are revolting without knowing against, or for, what. It seems that we are viewing a phenomenon—violence—which serves multiple functions. Some elements are logical and realistically purposeful, others are regressive and release destructive behavior, as evidenced by the slogan: "To hell with reality."

Let us look now at a few of the ideas presented in the papers of this conference, as they fall into various categories.

Whether aggression is of genetic origin or learned, it is present in all animals as a necessary drive for survival. It ensures territorial rights and sexual dominance when these are threatened. But this aggression usually ceases on defeat of the intruder—except in man who directs his drive toward members of his own species to the end of death. Some men are more, some less violent, although deep down all of us are killers.

Are the more violent born different with an XYY chromosome? Have they developed through early experiences into so-called sociopaths, psychopathic personalities or immature characters who lead others into violent scenes by fomenting mobs into regressive behavior? Do these leaders have organic brain changes plus inadequate socialization? To these questions we have few answers.

I think it may be safely stated that certain leaders foment violence, which in itself is contagious. Some homicidal children are subtly commanded by their parents to become violent. Television and other news media portray a violent society influencing those with no internal counteracting forces. Even Congress will not enact an effective gun-control bill. Yet these issues are secondary to the general social attitudes and changing moral values.

There is a decided difference between individual interpersonal violence and the wider social violence. Spiegel[1] lists several propositions related to social violence which, in the ghetto, he believes is due to the failure of the civil rights movement, while others blame increasing but insufficient success of that movement. He includes grievances, hostile belief systems, failures of communication and failures of social controls. Precipitating incidents trigger off a confrontation of mobs and police, resulting in an intoxicating angry "Roman Holiday" with final polarization of white against black.

On the basis of historical analogies, Spiegel attempts to develop a dialectic relationship between reconstructionists who "have not" and strive to "have," and nativists who resist change. He states that we have an historical amnesia for the traditional American violence. However, he suggests that today the reconstructionists who seemingly want to change the establishment really want a "piece of the action," after which they turn against future dissidents. The middle class black or even the indigenous worker who has "made it" deserts his own people—but he still participates in the Roman Holiday phase of burning and looting. To legitimize these concepts requires the neglect of a broader focus on other countries where the same processes are occurring. I believe our contemporary rapid systems of communications only set off separate foci of latent revolutionary violence awaiting a signal for eruption. True, America has given the signal.

Rubenstein[2] indicates that violence is not particular to American life and that we are not an exceptionally sick society. He states that violence has been written out of American history and the myth of peaceful progress substituted. Negroes are not unique but historically they are at the end of a long line of violence which is as American as apple pie, according to Rap Brown. Rubenstein states that violence occurs after established procedures have been tried and failed (the threshold concept). Even the current two party system has not offered choices. Thus solutions are sought outside of constitutional procedures as a means of transferring power.

Many recent events and conditions have been considered causal: the war, assasinations, use of drugs, over-permissiveness in child rearing, absence of extended families, etc. What this potpourri indicates to me is that we are operating on multiple levels of discourse such as:

biological: genetic, brain damage, drugs
psychological: maturation, developmental, personality deformation
social: rapid changes in living, absent nuclear family, working mother, social mobility, etc.

As in all multidisciplinary approaches these are difficult to articulate. West attempts to view violence within a life cycle model.[3] This is a logical method of analysis which views different causes and expressions of violence at each phase. By this approach West portrays a transition of violence as a central factor from personality development to social behavior. The question always remains whether we can extrapolate from individual psychology to group process. Nevertheless West portrays the steps and shifts of aggressive behavior from infantile omnipotence to adult life at which time the expected high level of conformity bottles up hostility and displaces it on to the stranger outside the group. Actually we as adults are often envious of youth evidenced in adults; phoney youthfulness. Would we like to live our lives over again— especially after the sexual revolution? Not I, even though with a glance at any woman I can see what in my youth it took two hours of hard work to get to.

Many years ago in our dialogues Spiegel and I speculated on the fate of bottled-up aggression. As a reformed neurologist I believed that the vast neuropil of the frontal lobes, lacking localization of function, might evolve into functioning in the service of control or sublimatory mechanisms. We also believed we needed a stranger, if mankind were to form a friendly conspecies group, and suggested that we find him in outer space.

The youth movement, representing a newly recognized phase of the life-cycle between adolescence and adulthood, has been the central focus of violence. The delay before the final choice of career-line or future life-style permits an opportunity for organized or unorganized attempts to change the existing adult social order before "commitment" to it. This may be a new phase of moratorium supposedly only characteristic of adolescence. Often considered as aggressors against society, youth accept the assigned role because it fits their own needs, or they remain "unaffiliated."

The adolescent and the youth seem to search for issues and they find them. Like the basic truth underlying a pathological paranoia the student activists have justifications. But as they combine their cries against war with their struggles against inadequate educational systems, they violently destroy and become in truth warriors and dropouts from school. They prove and accentuate what they apparently protest, just as the blacks destroy their own neighborhoods.

In recruiting surgical residents from our hospital for the expected riots at the Democratic Convention, we were told that there must be bloodshed. The demand to get hurt was to indicate the inadequacies and *savagery* of the power establishment against the downtrodden. Protesters use one rationalization or another and often fail to present constructive ideas so that beyond protest there are few positive elements. Is this a different kind of violence than the often quoted historical violent crises? The political radical-left has opportunistically used the adolescent hippies, yippies, and other youth for their own purposes to destroy.

Kenniston states that the leaders of the New Left are the brightest youngsters in their classes.[4] With no organization and no obvious course other than destruction, they influence the emotionality of a larger number of followers.

I think as psychiatrists we have looked at the "ego functions" of the violent social groups in a manner unlike our way of viewing individuals. We have tried to see the purposeful logical causes which in individuals we treat as rationalizations. We should look also at the underlying emotionality of our times released by deterioration of a number of social and political controls. I believe that most of the logical issues are false and that resolving many of them will only displace a so-called cause to another rationalized issue.

As Frank states, the violence between groups transcending the individual is sparked by ideological motives whose end point is never clear because it is destructive to the other groups, democracy, or the nation.[5] This gives meaning to existence. Internationally as well as in the ghetto what is needed, in addition to aid of all sorts, are self-esteem, pride, dignity and autonomy, and the freedom of people to make their own mistakes. Often in individual murders we sympathize not with the killed who cannot be helped, but hope that the killer who fights for his life can escape death. In a similar way we have a tendency to favor the aggressor even though he has killed the very law and order by which we and he survive.

I cannot say from what the world-wide violence results nor can I identify the emotional source for mob rule. It represents a justifiable movement based on real and logical issues *only in part*. It seems more likely to be an international, cataclysmic, threshold-breaking change in our society, exploding and spreading with the speed of our electronic communication systems.

Kolb indicated that what we need and do not have, is a theory with predictable power for control of violence.[6] I take exception to that focus. My frame of reference as a psychiatrist, not a social scientist, is to question how so many restricted and constricted people with some form of modern neuroses and possessing little of the histrionic neuroses and psychoses of the past, contributed to the current state of group violence.

There may be a clue in the increasing number of patients with the borderline syndrome, who have little or no capacity for affectionate relationships or consistency in maintaining a relationship with love-objects. As a result, aggression necessary for both survival and creativity extends beyond the optimum and controllable level.

All major religions indicate the universal function of love. The psychoanalytic theory of neutralized aggression spells it out clearly, and Toynbee indicates that for survival a new world religion is necessary.[7] The organization called Mankind espouses the development of the conspecies mankind as a concept necessary for survival.

Why are so many people deficient in the ability to sustain affection? There seems to be little belief in or expectancy of personal or family survival and in the absence of an extended family, little experience in collateral relationships. What is left is either individualism or authoritarian dominance, with little hope of change within a reasonable time. If love is lost, then hate triumphs.

No one can doubt that all is not well in our expanding society even though not one of the defects that is pin-pointed by a specific name is a new problem. All have existed for decades, even centuries, as characteristics of civilizations that spawn major urban concentrations which in turn tend to destroy the civilizations in which they develop. Under these circumstances the balance between personal and community life vacillates and often becomes precarious.

What we call revolution, although this word has become denigrated to mean almost any kind of dissent, as distinguished from evolution is a matter of speed of change. One is rapid and seems to constitute, or is interpreted as, a crisis. The other is much slower and often imperceptible except in retrospect. Most violent national revolutions with the goals of greater freedom have been followed by periods of tyranny with the major outstanding exception of the American Revolution.

Evolutions whether biological or social are often regressive as in mutations which are most frequently lethal. So the end result of either is not necessarily progress, but this is a value judgment better left to posterity.

Yet I do not believe that we are witnessing a revolution nor the beginnings of one that threatens our established system of government, although violence is rampant in various focal confrontations such as the racial, the student, the anti-war and other movements of protest. Various explanations have been offered as causes by persons whose professions lead them to specific biases. The psychologist talks about student paranoia, the sociologist about a characteristic violent American society—or conflict between have and have-nots—, the psychiatrist about racist and generational hate and guilt. But these are derived from frames of reference too close to the behaviors and too narrow for inclusive generalities.

I believe that we are witnessing at all levels of our social network a conflict based on dualistic thinking, the polarities of which are personal or individual freedom as against social structures maintaining the functions of regulation and control. Each has moved speedily and quantitatively to become antagonistic and reactionary to the other. The greater the demand for freedom, the more repressive measures are set into action. The more restrictive controls to dampen freedoms, the more protest and violence as the final common pathway of many causes.

With this frame of reference no single cause can be accepted, instead a general approach to *organization* essential to all of life, whether biological, psychological or social, is more adequate. It is best epitomized by Paul Weiss[8] who in discussing organization from cell to culture wrote: "I mean the operation of a principle of order that stabilizes and preserves the total pattern of the group activity of a huge mass of semi-autonomous elements."

With rigid order we have tyranny, with no order we have anarchy. What we need is "order in the gross and freedom in the small." This is a unitary form of thinking toward which man has been evolving for centuries. Those who have preached or practiced it have not been especially successful for it is difficult to maintain in the midst of stress and its evoked emotional responses, as indicated by the use of the term "crisis." This should designate a temporary blip on a gradually moving trend-line. It is particularly difficult for those who need the myth of single causes and promises of supernatural solutions, to accept this kind of thinking.

In current times we are witnessing back and forth swings in control and expression, only different from previous decades in the rapidity and the range of the shifts of emphasis. Also, the emotionality of commitment results, on the one hand, in the destruction of the protestors *own* environment whether these be blacks' housing, students' school buildings or organizations' principles; and, on the other hand, the emotionality of the regulators of order results in gassing, shooting and severe prison sentences. Reason always fails, temporarily, before the onslaught of mass irrationality.

We are engaged in rapid changes associated with turbulence and violent clashes between each interface of an artificial dichotomy in our thinking feeling and behavior, intensified by divisive speeches and actions of our national administration. I predict that the intensity of the current struggle will now decrease as long as our useless war in Indo-China continues. Then the conflict will continue although muted, and become less *against* a focus and more *for* constructive changes. It is already turning in that direction. In a political sense, hopefully the trend will be more toward increased individual freedom and not the regressive license, and drug-excited irresponsibility, acting out Dosteovsky's words, "One has to be mad to become oneself".

I do not use the term "freedom" literally, but in the American sense related to overcoming barriers of limitations and to establishing new and non-geographical frontiers. These are evidenced in the search for new experiences, and dreams of a better world focused on other than excessive material advantages; experiences that transcend homeostatic and sociostatic traditionally set goals. Goal changing thinking and behaviors are erroneously called radical only because of their form and not because of their innovative contents. Instead, they are the hopes for progress.

We should educate the young to the fallacy of "instant solutions", non-negotiable demands, and militant confrontations instead of imitating them as even some professionals are doing. These are like cries in the night that things are bad. The hungry child has a crying crisis before each delayed feeding, but feeding him is only a temporary solution; he will get hungry again. Eventually, he learns to wait more or less patiently and for longer periods when he *internalizes confidence that his needs will be met at least in part.*

As adults we should understand the meaning of the cries of protest from the youth and our role in instilling confidence that we are heeding them and that within our powers we will help to encourage personal freedoms and reconsiderations of values that have personal relevance within efficient, regulatory but permissive social controls which in themselves are capable of change.

REFERENCES

1. Spiegel, J.: *Toward a Theory of Collective Violence,* "Perspectives in Violence and Aggression," American Medical Association, Chicago, 1970.
2. Rubenstein, R.: Presentation of the AMA-APA Regional Conference on Violence and Aggression, Nov. 1968.
3. West, L. J.: Presentation of the AMA-APA Regional Conference on Violence and Aggression, Nov. 1968.
4. Keniston, K.: *The Uncommitted: Alienated Youth in American Society,* Harcourt Brace, New York, 1967.
5. Frank, J. D.: *Psychological Aspects of International Violence,* "Perspectives in Violence and Aggression," American Medical Association, Chicago, 1970.
6. Kolb, L. C.: *Violence and Aggression: An Overview,* "Perspectives in Violence and Aggression," American Medical Association, Chicago, 1970.
7. Toynbee, A.: *A Study of History,* 12 volumes, Oxford University Press, London, England 1934-1961.
8. Weiss, P.A.: Living Nature and the Knowledge Gap, *Saturday Review,* 29:19, Nov. 1969.

SECTION II

CLINICAL PERSPECTIVES

This section, focusing on the violent individual in a medical-psychological perspective, offers many practical clinical implications. Physicians and mental health professionals are often confronted with requests for evaluation of potentially violent individuals or situations, and are therefore frequently able to help prevent violent behavior. Dr. Roy Menninger and Dr. Herbert C. Modlin provide an excellent review of the literature pertinent to the prediction and prevention of violent behavior.

The study of "The Self-Referred Violent Patient" by Dr. Lion et al, tends to stress further the crucial role that crisis oriented interventions can play in preventing expressions of violent and destructive impulses. We are told that active interventions *can* help to avoid violence and, reluctance not withstanding, that our efforts most often will result in relief and appreciation from the individual on the brink of violence. This knowledge is valuable because often a fear of retaliation prevents the clinician from "getting involved" or intervening in a situation where violent behavior is imminent, even though the patient may be asking clearly for control. This paper, as that of Dr. Mortimer Gross, stresses also the importance of organic factors in the treatment of patients subject to outbursts of violence.

Dr. Michael Kalogerakis' paper on homicidal adolescents provides further valuable clinical information relevant to the evaluation of the violence-prone patient. Here we see similarities between Dr. Kalogerakis' clinical experience and the significant clinical features reported in previous papers.

"The Lethal Situation" as described by Dr. Douglas Sargent adds yet another important set of considerations: the dimension of interpersonal communication, and our understanding of the genesis of situations that result in violent behavior. Dr. Sargent raises important questions concerning the possible effects of mass media, particularly television and movies, in the development of predispositions toward violent behavior based on observations of the communication of violent wishes in the family setting.

Some interesting psychodynamic considerations of the genesis of violent feelings and impulses, as well as possible adaptive effects of certain routes of expression of violent feelings, are discussed in clinical papers by Dr. Peter Giovacchini and Dr. Richard Chessick. Drs. Muslin and Pieper raise some unanswered questions concerning the loss of ego-control in a paper describing an impulsive murder committed by a student, without a history which might have predicted this behavior.

These three papers underscore the continuing contributions of psychodynamic considerations developed through the clinical case study of violent individuals. The entire section attests to the importance of a balanced and comprehensive study of clinical characteristics, individual history, and interpersonal and individual psychodynamics in our attempts to understand and control inter-human violence.

INDIVIDUAL VIOLENCE:
PREVENTION IN THE VIOLENCE-
THREATENING PATIENT

Roy W. Menninger, M.D. and
Herbert C. Modlin, M.D.

The current national preoccupation with violence has caused a sharp upswing in attention to the problems of violence. To define and understand the context in which much violence is occurring, and the factors which appear to provoke and sustain it, a substantial part of this attention has been centered on its socio-psychological aspects. In this perspective, an act of individual violence has significance chiefly as another statistic, unless, as in an assassination, it acquires, through its dramatic features, a uniqueness apart from "usual" violent acts and thus is made seemingly incomprehensible.

Our focus here is not on the violent act after the fact but on the violence-threatening patient, with emphasis on the possibilities of prevention. Many physicians have been, are, and will be confronted by persons who threaten to become violent, or persons whose manner or comment prompts physicians to wonder anxiously, "might he indeed become violent with someone?" To review characteristics of such patients and offer some observations about the options for intervention constitute the intent of this paper. Although suicide is not centrally discussed, the interchangeability of self-directed and other-directed aggression will become obvious.

In the initial interview the physician listens to the patient—not an easy task when hints of potential violence begin to mobilize the physician's own anxiety. In the service of enabling the physician to assess the degree of threat and at the same time experience reduction of his own anxiety by investing himself in a clearly defined task, we would set forth a series of cues and clues as guides to what he should listen and look for:

1. *Fears of or concerns about losing control.* Often the apprehension will be ill-defined or non-specific, expressed by the patient as feeling he may "blow

---

Dr. Menninger is president of the Menninger Foundation, Topeka, Kansas; Dr. Modlin serves as director of the Foundation's Department of Preventive Psychiatry.

his top." In spite of the vagueness of his description, the patient may impose a sense of discomfort or anxiety on the physician himself akin to the phenomenon of "primal anxiety" described by Fischer and Klin.[1] However, the violence-threatening patient may be considerably more specific, actually threatening violence to a particular person.

As in the case of a patient who speaks of suicide, the threat should be heeded and taken at its face value until or unless events and additional evidence dictate otherwise. In one series[2] three of four persons who murdered without apparent motive had conveyed to someone their fears of losing control before the murders took place—and in each case, the warnings were disregarded.

In his series on homicide-threatening patients, MacDonald[3] observed that a threat made in the absence of much provocation suggests a greater risk of violence than a threat made in response to extreme provocation.

The apprehension of losing control may be expressed in a somewhat different form as a kind of global hostility, with the manifestly loosened thought patterns and paranoid distortions characteristic of the "Whitman Syndrome" described by Kuehn and Burton.[4]

2. *Evidence that the person has been looking for help,* however obscure his methods. There may be indications of doctor-shopping, frequently for seemingly minor complaints, but with a quality of persistence and anxiety; or reports of seeing the minister, bothering the neighbors, telephoning mother three times in one week, calling a lawyer but failing to keep an appointment. Any of these maneuvers may suggest that the patient is restlessly seeking connection with someone who can help him gain relief from his threatening internal pressures.

3. *Reports of suggestive actions.* The patient has been observed by his wife to be cleaning or examining his gun without any such obvious purpose as hunting; or is known to have just purchased a gun or ammunition; or is reported to have driven at 90 miles an hour down the highway after quarreling with his wife.

A woman complains of uneasiness bordering on panic each time she works in the kitchen. Well-directed inquiry will reveal her frightening impulse to jab a knife into her child.

Another housewife reports having thrown out all the pills in the medicine cabinet. A pediatrician hears from a mother that her husband has lost his tolerance for the baby's crying and burst out of the house the night before, presumably to avoid harming the child. At times the behavior is more bluntly suggestive: a woman reports that her husband has nearly strangled her on two occasions recently or, when drunk, has threatened her with a knife.

It is impressive to note how often after such allusive actions—with firearms, for example—there is unequivocal evidence that the spouse has done nothing at all to have the gun or guns removed from ready access to the violence-threatening patient. This happens so commonly that suspecting unconscious collusion to promote the violent act is unavoidable. This aspect of offender-victim collusion will be referred to further. Easy availability of firearms to the violence-threatening patient makes more pertinent Shakespeare's observation in *King John:* "How oft the sight of means to do ill deeds, makes ill deeds done." [5]

A review of the patient's past history may uncover the following features particularly relevant to assessment of the violence-threatening patient:

1. *Episodes of altered states of consciousness.* Frequently reported in connection with earlier episodes of violence are dissociative trance-like states or "black-outs" during the period of violent behavior and concerning which the patient may have some degree of amnesia.[2] The temporal lobe dyscontrol syndrome described by Ervin[6] and Schwab[7] has been implied as etiologic in a significant number of violent episodes, with evidence that surgical intervention may favorably alter the pattern.

2. *Previous homicides.* Not unusually these are reported spontaneously; yet more often than may be realized, they have occurred but are disguised. In his series of 80 consecutive threat-to-kill admissions, MacDonald found two with a history of previous homicides, several of them presented as quasi-legitimate (having occurred while on guard duty, etc.).[8]

3. *Previous assaults.* A history of attacks, particularly those inflicting physical injury and associated with other forms of violence, suggests chronically low anxiety, anger and frustration thresholds and life-long difficulty in controlling aggressive impulses.

4. *Previous suicide attempts.* In MacDonald's series,[3] the violence-threatening patient with no record of previous suicide attempts was more prone to commit homicidal violence; and conversely, those who had previously attempted suicide were more likely to kill themselves than someone else. The incidence of suicide following murder, however, is surprisingly high. According to Wolfgang, more murderers kill themselves than are executed;[9] and it is reported that in England between 1952 and 1960, one-third of all murderers committed suicide.[10]

In evaluating the patient's immediate situation, the physician must scrutinize the nature of the patient's relationships with persons significant to him, and reality factors in his current environment that could trigger violent response.

The trigger factors are stressful through their capacity to evoke reactions of rage: frustrations in efforts to gain or maintain status, security and reputation, or events or actions of others erosive of self-esteem. Thus, discovery of infidelity, humiliations, insults, loss through separation or death of an ambivalently held spouse or parent are highly likely to stimulate the vulnerable patient to violence. Such triggering factors ordinarily exist in the immediate setting of the violence-threatening patient.

A careful survey of his intimate associates commonly reveals the presence of persons kept close to the patient by intensely ambivalent ties, with signs of considerable verbal or physical sado-masochistic behaviors between them. It is the nature of these relationships to be both sustained and chronically disrupted by mutually provocative hurtful acts, with each person taunting the other to the limits of tolerance—and sometimes beyond.

One series[11] estimates that in 26 percent of 588 criminal homicides, the victim was the first to show and use a deadly weapon, or strike a blow—in effect, was the initiator of violent interplay.

MacDonald[3] describes a dramatic example of the cooperative sado-masochistic behavior in the case of "a 21-year-old man who asked his girl friend if she loved him. When she replied, 'If you don't know now, you never will,' he struck her on the back of the head, knocking her down. Then he shot her in the head, in each hand, and in the right shoulder. He then dragged her into the bathroom and tried to drown her. She fought her way out of the bathroom and he pulled her into the bedroom, where he tried to smother her. Charges of assault to murder were withdrawn after his girl friend married him and refused to testify against him."

Schultz has described the need for a clearer understanding of the victim-offender relationship and proposed that this area of inquiry, rich in its multiple implications, be called "victimology."[12] In some homicides, the victim had behaved so provocatively that it must be assumed he used the killer as an instrument of suicide. Wolfgang found that more than half the victims in his series had the characteristics of offenders, documented by previous arrests for crimes of violence, and that in many of the relationships mere chance determined which of the pair was victim and which offender.[13]

While the "incomprehensible" crimes of a Speck or Whitman generate a stereotype of "faceless violence" (a sudden wholly unpredictable outburst of violence against unknown and innocent persons), the most frequent patterns of violent acts involve persons well known to, or at least acquainted with, the offender.

In a study of more than 200 violent assaults, 38 percent of the victims were found to be members of the offender's family and 40 percent his friends.[14] Examination of a series of 186 murderers in Illinois prisons revealed that they knew 85 percent of their victims well; 7 percent were acquaintances, such as prostitutes; and only 8 percent were complete strangers.[14]

Exploration of the patient's *early history*, if it can be obtained, may reveal clues predictive of possible violence. When applicable, any of the following will suggest high probability that the patient may express loss of control in a violent attack upon someone:

1. *Severe emotional deprivation or overt rejection in childhood:* prolonged absence of one or both parents, a chaotic family life, or actual removal of the child from his family to live with friends or relatives.

2. *Parental seduction:* ranging from subtle forms such as offsprings' sharing their parents' bedroom through adolescence; through overt actions such as a mother's bathing the early adolescent boy, or parading nude before him, or a father's forbidding his four adolescent daughters ever to close the bathroom door under any circumstances, or inflicting painful corporal punishment; to frank incest.

3. *Exposure to brutality and extreme violence:* witnessing violent episodes involving parents, neighbors, or others in the community, and/or being subjected to violent attacks and punishments by parents or parent-surrogates. This witnessed and/or experienced violence is often associated with sexual behavior. As has been suggested,[2] the association of violence and sexual activity in a child's early years probably stimulates unwholesome fantasies about the sexual act as something overwhelmingly violent and sadistic.

4. *Childhood fire-setting:* "accidental" arson, building bonfires, homemade fire bombs, etc.

5. *Cruelty to animals or other children:* as evidenced by intentional destruction or injury of a sadistic sort; setting fire to animals, torturing them, etc.

The three latter points may be especially pertinent. A psychiatric study of 84 prisoners by Hellman and Blackman[15] demonstrated that all or part of the triad of enuresis, fire-setting and cruelty to animals marked the early history of 74 percent of those who had committed violent, aggressive crimes, compared with only 28 percent of those who had committed no violent antisocial acts. The authors indeed suggest that this triad be considered pathognomonic of seriously troubled behavior highly liable to become violently expressive in later life.

All the above five points are suggestive of disturbed parent-child relationships, and distorted perceptions of self and others that may predispose to violent response in a provocative situation. One noteworthy effort to study these factors in a controlled way[3] revealed significant differences among a homicide-threat group, a convicted criminal homicide-offender group, and a control group, *only* with reference to suicidal attempts and arson.

However, the incidence of four factors (parental brutality, parental seduction, childhood fire-setting, and cruelty to animals), when considered together, was higher in both the homicide-threat and the homicide-offender groups than in the control group.

A composite picture drawn from psychological examination of violence-threatening patients is at best only partially accurate, because a potential for violence is presumed present in everyone, given sufficient provocation, and because a person liable to violent behavior may manifest any of a variety of clinical psychiatric syndromes.

One may characterize these patients, however, in terms of a) meager tolerance for anxiety and tension, b) proneness to action rather than to such psychic-delay mechanisms as thought, words and symbols, and c) limited, superficial, or highly ambivalent relations with persons who are significant in their worlds. Their perceptions are frequently distorted by their suspicious assumptions about the actions and intentions of others, especially those most involved with them, and by their hypertrophied sensitivity about themselves.

Intensely self-centered, they may paradoxically see others as very powerful, feel themselves to be weak, inferior and inadequate, especially (if male) in relationship to women. Their low anxiety tolerance, coupled with a predilection for motoric self-expression, makes physical violence an understandable reaction to pressures or stresses which may overwhelm their poverty of psychic mechanisms, even when the stress is relatively trivial.

Often the patients' surface appearance of overcontrol and inhibition rapidly gives way, under pressure, to hyperactivity and erratic behavior. In their paper regarding such patients, Satten, et al, describe an "all-or-none" quality of response—once their meager controls are overtaxed, they are flooded with affect. Morbid fantasy and a tendency to immediate, unreflective and usually destructive action ensue.[2]

Intervention

Such cues and clues as the foregoing constitute a clear sign that the patient is calling for help, even though he "sends" his message in an obscure and indirect code. The fact of his coming to the doctor's office communicates his presentiment of reduced self-control, impaired judgment or inability to handle stresses in his immediate environment. He approaches the physician, not necessarily from a recognition that he is sick, but more from sensing that the physician can understand, and with understanding should be able to intervene in behalf of that struggling part of himself in need of augmented controls against the threatened breakthrough of destructive urges. The physician must take the message and read it seriously.

In his efforts to intervene the physician should gauge the need to supplement the patient's failing psychic functions and should consider the following:

1. *Controls.* Provide medication to reduce tension and activity to safer levels; solicit supportive companionship or relative or friend; arrange for protective hospitalization.

2. *Judgment.* Assist the patient to think and talk about his problems; correct distorted perceptions and ideas by presenting the reality of the situation insistently and persistently.

3. *Environment.* Interview the stressful or also distressed or provocative or fearful spouse, girl friend, etc., preferably with the patient, and attempt to alter the strained relationship; remove the patient from the stressful situation through an out-of-town trip, vacation from the job, or moving out of the home temporarily.

Intervention to help may produce a reaction of irrational resistance in the patient, denial that he needs what the physician recommends, and insistence that he is really quite capable of mobilizing the self-control he temporarily lacks. Such resistance reflects the patient's extreme ambivalence, part of his inability to cope with his impulse to violence in the first place. It is crucial, therefore, for the physician not to be misled by the patient's seeming resurgence of strength, or by some anxious wish of his own to see the patient get better fast. He must concentrate instead on the patient's *initial* message— the real one, the one to which he must respond.

In its essence, the basis for intervention is the physician's humanistic and medical ethic: that he act to support life and prevent or mitigate forces of pain, injury and death. This position enables the physician to invoke sufficient resources to fulfill his ethical commitment without resort to moralistic, unitive or legalistic arguments or justification.

The physician structures his work with the patient on the realization that the violence-threatening patient feels and believes violence to be the sole exit from his stress-bound box of life. Resort to violence bespeaks the despair which comes from failure to have, or to perceive, any alternatives. The task therefore is to help the patient search effectively for alternatives, and to conduct this search by a method he is neither well accustomed to nor adequately trained in: the use of words and thought.

This unaccustomed recourse to speech is a means by which part of the destructive energy can be safely drained off, thereby obviating its being spent in destructive action. By catalyzing the accompanying discharge of emotional energy, speech inseparable from thought becomes the means by which the patient can recognize and define actions alternative to the violence he had believed would be his only possible coping device. The physician, through his active participation in the talking-thinking process, promotes the accruing impulse control generated by the developing doctor-patient relationship.

By questioning the patient about the immediate threat of violence, about alternatives to it, about the consequences of various possible actions (including the self-destructive violent ones), about his unrealized aims and hopes and needs, the physician simultaneously fosters the search for violence-avoiding alternatives, and teaches a method of problem-solving the patient can learn and use.

Clearly the physician's helping efforts, subject to the patient's own limitations and capacities, may not be instantaneously fruitful, and thus he should move promptly to obtain sufficient control, such as hospitalization, medication and police constraint. Because this is a temporary intervention at a time of crisis, it is imperative that the physician engage other resources in whatever (possibly complex and long-term) supportive or deterrent measures may be required: the patient's family, minister, lawyer, social agencies and appropriate psychiatric facilities.

What the physician can provide is the crucial service of early recognition and initial intervention which may ultimately determine the difference between successful prevention and disastrous violence.

Summary

The violence-threatening patient who confronts the physician is discussed in terms of medical intervention designed to forestall violent action. The success of such moves depends upon the physician's readiness to perceive the behavioral and verbal clues that point to a potential for violent behavior, and upon his ability to recognize the special nature of measures he can apply.

REFERENCES

1. Fischer, H.K., and Klin, B.M.: Postgrad Med. 30:200, 1961.
2. Satten, J., Menninger, K.A., Rosen, I. and Mayman, M.: Amer J Psychiat 117:48, 1960.
3. MacDonald, J.M.: Amer J Psychiat 124:457, 1967.
4. Kuehn, J.L., and Burton, J.: Psychiatric Spectator 5(5):12, 1968.
5. Shakespeare, W.: King John IV, ii.
6. Ervin, F.: Epstein, A.W., and King, H.E.: Arch Neurol Psychiat 74:488, 1955.
7. Schwab, R.S., Sweet, W.H., Mark, Vernon H., Kjillberg, R.M., and Ervin, F.R.: Trans Amer Neurol Ass 90:12, 1965.
8. MacDonald, J.M.: Amer J Psychiat 120:125, 1963.
9. Wolfgang, M.E., Kelly, A., and Nolde, H.C.: J Crim Law, Criminol & Police Sci 53:301, 1962.
10. Gibson, E., and Klein, S.: Murder, London, H.M. Stationary Office. 1961.
11. Wolfgang, M.E.: Patterns in Criminal Homicide, Philadelphia, U. Pa., 1958.
12. Schultz, L.G.: Crime and Del. 14:135, 1960.
13. Wolfgang, M.E.: J Crim Law, Criminal & Plice Sci 48:1, 1957.
14. Clark, R.: Associated Press Release from Miami, Fla. Detroit Free Press, P. 8A, 1967.
15. Hellman, D.S., and Blackman, N.: Amer J Psychiat 122:1431, 1966.

THE SELF-REFERRED VIOLENT PATIENT

John R. Lion, M.D., George Bach-y-Rita, M.D.

and Frank R. Ervin, M.D.

Introduction

Because the stigma attached to mental health problems is waning, an increasing number of patients now enter hospitals voluntarily with chief complaints of episodic violence, impulsiveness and destructive urges. To the physician in hospital or emergency room practice, these patients may express vague fears of aggression ("I'm afraid I'm going to break something"), more specific homicidal ideation ("I want to kill my wife") or descriptions of past acts of violence ("I hurt people for no reason").

Proper evaluation of potentially violent patients is often difficult. The physician is hampered by the urgency of the patient's problems and the potential danger that the patient poses for the community. If the physician makes a hasty disposition, he may never determine the etiology of the violent patient's behavior.

Yet, there are certain diagnostic techniques which the physician can use when evaluating such a patient. It is the purpose of this paper to furnish guidelines for handling the violent patient and evaluating the etiology of his violence.

Controls

Patients entering a medical facility with complaints of violent acts or impulsiveness differ widely in degrees of accompanying anxiety. Some patients are lucid and rational; others are greatly agitated. The acutely disturbed

Dr. Lion is staff psychiatrist, Department of Neuropsychiatry, United States Naval Hospital, Philadelphia, Pennsylvania; Dr. Bach-y-Rita is director of inpatient/partial care service at Marin County General Hospital Community Mental Health Center, San Francisco, California; and Dr. Ervin serves as associate professor of psychiatry at Harvard Medical School and director of the Stanley Cobb Laboratories for Psychiatric Research, Massachusetts General Hospital, Boston, Massachusetts.

patient requires immediate and firm controls. The physician can interpret the patient's severe anxiety as a manifestation of a fear that he will act on his impulses. The physician should assure the patient that his violent impulses will be checked.

Medication
Often the acutely disturbed patient benefits from medication which diminishes his anxiety and reduces his fantasies. The phenothiazines remain the drugs of choice in these instances. The patient can be helped more effectively when medication has calmed him and he is again in control of his impulses.

Security
When dealing with the acutely disturbed patient, the physician should feel free to summon the aid of security personnel. He need not be afraid that this move will frighten the patient. The presence of such aides helps to convince the patient that his impulses will be held in check and that external controls are present. In addition, the presence of security personnel allays the doctor's fears. His own tensions are reduced—not transmitted to the patient—and the stresses between doctor and patient are significantly eased.

Hospitalization
The degree of agitation among patients differs, and the indications for hospitalization of violent patients varies with their acute states. (The more violent the patient and the less he is in control of his impulses, the greater the indication for hospitalization.)

But, the patient's threats are just as important as his behavior. The physician should take seriously threats of any kind, no matter how calmly uttered. If the patient alleges that he will harm someone, (or is afraid of harming someone) and does not elaborate on the nature or object of this potential act, he still should be taken seriously. Diffuseness of intent may mask a deep underlying conflict.

Many physicians harbor fantasies of retaliation when they hospitalize violent patients who oppose such confinement. However, our experience suggests that no such ill effects result from enforced hospitalization. Although the patient may express strong objections to enforced confinement, he usually feels genuine relief and a lessening of anxiety and impulsive thinking when told firmly that he will be placed in the hospital.

The concept of hospitalization should be presented to the patient in a therapeutic way, i.e., that the physician is very much concerned about the patient's potential danger to himself and others and that confinement will last no longer than necessary. Hospitalization does not mean commitment. Rather, it means limited confinement for purposes of observation. The patient should be encouraged to return to the referring facility when his difficulty is over and he has been released from the hospital. This assurance conveys to the patient the idea that the doctor is interested in him and is willing to see him again. Hence, the patient does not view hospitalization as a rejection by the physician.

Genuine concern by the physician can make a lasting impression on the patient. It may even convert hostile and paranoid individuals into cooperative patients. Even a letter to the patient sent to the hospital reassures him of the concern of the physician who initiated hospitalization. Enforced hospitalization when accomplished in a sympathetic way conveys to the patient the fact that someone cares enough about him to protect him from harm.

Patients who enter emergency room facilities with a specific request for hospitalization should be taken seriously and confined according to their wishes. Often, such patients realize that dangerous impulses may erupt. They are seeking some form of control.

Some patients who have agreed to necessary hospitalization change their minds while waiting for confirmation and completion of the necessary arrangements. With the delay, the patient's acute anxiety and impulsiveness may suddenly reappear. The physician should anticipate this possibility. He can reduce these difficulties by having security personnel attend the patient during the stressful period between leaving the hospital and arriving at another facility. An ambulance should always be used in transporting the patient to another hospital.

Careful History

Whether or not the violent patient requires hospitalization, it is the physician's responsibility to obtain a careful history. The physician should not assume that the patient has been cured once his anxiety has abated and/or hospitalization has been arranged. On the contrary, the physician has done nothing thus far to ascertain the etiology of the patient's violence. This diagnosis is just as important as calming the patient when he is in an acute state. Several diagnostic techniques can help in the determination of the probable causes of the patient's violence.

In ascertaining the causes of the patient's violent behavior, the physician must try to determine whether the patient's difficulties result from neurological problems or psychiatric problems, or both. Physicians often treat violent patients only by traditional psychiatric methods. Malamud,[1] for example, has shown that patients with psychiatric complaints, including violence, are given inadequate organic evaluation.

Clues to Neurological Difficulties

The patient's violent behavior may be caused by a neurological disorder such as a brain tumor or temporal lobe epilepsy. The physician should investigate symptoms such as headache or altered states of consciousness which may accompany the violent act or impulsiveness.

Are there subtle personality changes which have occurred over time and which may represent a slow growing neoplasm in the frontal lobe?[2] Relatives may provide more information about such changes.

Is there a marked alteration in sexual function or memory which suggests a temporal lobe process?[3]

Is there a past history of infection such as meningitis or other trauma which may have led to brain damage? Is there an impairment of intelligence or a history of learning difficulty?

Is there a family history of epilepsy or a history of convulsions in childhood? Do aura or seizure-like states occur? Is there a history of repetitive rage reactions or reoccurring temper tantrums which suggest temporal lobe epilepsy?[4]

If there are positive answers to any of the above questions, a neurological consultation is indicated. The neurologist may wish to perform a variety of tests, including a lumbar puncture, skull series, brain scan, or contrast studies. Multiple sleep EEG's may be necessary to confirm the diagnosis of temporal lobe epilepsy.[5]

Clues to Psychiatric Difficulties

Once neurological factors have been ruled out, the physician can attempt to assess the patient's psychological difficulties. A past history of parental brutality or sexual assault, eneuresis, pyromania, or cruelty to animals is particularly ominous with regard to the potential for violence.[6, 7]

Is the patient's job a potential hazard to himself or others? Does he, for example, drive a truck or bus or operate machinery? Has he been involved in serious automobile accidents or used a car as a means of dealing with stress? Do toxic factors such as alcohol or chronic drug use release his impulsiveness?

Does he own weapons that make it easier for him to act upon his impulses? Is there a significant past history of impulsive behavior? Suicide attempts may be an example of impulsive action. Is the patient seriously depressed, psychotic, or on the verge of psychosis?

Positive answers to any of the above conditions indicate the need for psychiatric consultation.

Psychiatric Treatment

Our impression has been that the largest group of patients with a fear of committing acts of violence falls into the classification of "borderline" or "schizoid" personality type.[8] Such patients are characterized by a history of severe emotional deprivation, unstable relationships, and a need for immediate gratification. It is evident that patients such as these cannot tolerate the anxiety produced by insight-oriented psychotherapy. Therapy should be modified so that it is of a more supportive nature.

A violent patient may not agree to see a physician at a regular time or for as long as an hour. But such a patient still can be helped if the physican is flexible. He can see the patient irregularly and for brief periods. An occasional interchange of 10 or 15 minutes may be enough to meet the violent patient's need for emotional support.

We routinely give our telephone number to violent patients and encourage them to call us when they think their impulses for violence are getting out of control. Drugs are an adjunct of treatment. Again, the phenothiazines have proved helpful for patients who are argumentative, paranoid or impulsive.

Goal of Treatment

Despite the best medical efforts, it may be difficult to eradicate the problems of the violent patient by traditional psychiatric methods. Still, the physician can try through supportive psychiatric treatment to ease the patient's conflicts. The physician can also urge the patient to contact him promptly when acute anxiety states begin or when impulses to behave in a violent manner get out of hand.

REFERENCES

1. Malamud, M.: Arch Neurol 17:113, 1967.
2. Strauss, I. and Keschner, M.: Arch Neurol & Psychiat 33:986, 1935.
3. Epstein, A.W.: J Nerv Ment Dis 133:247, 1961.
4. Treffert, D.A.: Amer J Psychiat 120:765, 1964.
5. Ervin, F. R.: *Comprehensive Textbook of Psychiatry*, A. Freedman & M. Kaplan (eds.), Williams & Wilkins, 1967.
6. Hellman, D.S. and Blackman, N.: Amer J Psychiat 122:1431, 1966.
7. MacDonald, J.M.: Amer J Psychiat 120:125, 1963.
8. Schmideberg, M.: *American Handbook of Psychiatry*, Vol. 1, S. Arieti (ed), Basic Books, New York, 1959.

VIOLENCE ASSOCIATED WITH ORGANIC BRAIN DISEASE

Mortimer D. Gross, M.D.

If we had a fully developed general systems theory of behavior, we could speak about all factors which contribute to violence: psychodynamic factors, cultural factors, neighborhood, religion, age, sex, etc. It would not be necessary to fragment human conditions and discuss only organic brain disease, as though it existed in a vacuum.

Unfortunately, such a developed theory does not exist, so it is necessary to isolate factors and discuss them one at a time. I am not suggesting that organic brain disease is the only factor in violence, or even a major factor. Organic brain disease does not exist in a vacuum, but in a person with a definite personality, living in a specific family in a particular culture.

Nevertheless, I believe organic brain disease has some specific relevance to violence, and in addition, there is the practical implication of control of some aspects of violence by treatment of the disease by medication.

The literature on this subject is confusing for several reasons. One is the definition of organic brain disease. Traditionally, such a disorder is characterized by confusion, memory loss, loss of abstractive abilities and loss of judgment. It is associated with such lesions as cell destruction due to senile brain disease, tumors, and trauma. There usually are neurologic signs as well as mental changes, and special psychological tests are quite conclusive diagnostically.

But recent advances in biochemistry, electron microscopy, and neurophysiology disclose much subtler aspects of organic brain disease, involving changes at a subcellular or molecular level. These changes do not produce major neurologic findings, but only "soft" neurologic signs, and psychologic tests frequently are inadequate to show evidence of "organicity."

Therefore, when the neurologist or psychologist finds "no evidence of

Dr. Gross is clinical assistant professor of psychiatry at the University of Illinois College of Medicine, Chicago.

organic brain disease," they are speaking of macroscopic or microscopic disease. They cannot rule out chemical or pathophysiologic disturbances at a submicroscopic or molecular level. One might ask how these disturbances can then be demonstrated. There is no good answer. The electro-encephalogram (EEG) may reveal pathophysiologic abnormalities, but even this is an assumption.

The logical pressure to assume minimal organic changes in the absence of truly hard evidence comes from the similarity in symptoms of those with proved macroscopic organic brain lesions, and of those with only minimal "soft" signs or an abnormal EEG. Biochemical studies are only now beginning to bridge this gap.

Another source of confusion is the role of the EEG. Some authors demonstrate that in a population with a high incidence of violence, there is also a high incidence of EEG abnormalities. But other authors claim that EEG "abnormalities" are so common that no conclusions can be drawn from such data. One control study of adolescent boys[1] showed 58 per cent with an "abnormal" EEG. Under these circumstances, how can one use the word "abnormal" in any meaningful way?

Most control studies[2, 3, 4, 5] show about 10 percent abnormal EEG's in children, a somewhat higher per cent in young adolescents, and lower in adulthood. The 58 per cent figure came from an all-night study of boys in a private school. One explanation for the high figure, apart from the long EEG sample, is the likelihood that the "controls" were not a typical population. Private schools are well-known as havens for children with behavior and learning problems.

Wilson conducted an EEG control study of 160 grade school and high school children. Because most of his patients were referred by school teachers as a result of behavior or learning problems, or both, he asked teachers to refer children for the control study who in their opinion were free of such problems. In 100 grade school children, there were *3 abnormalities, or 3%.* In 60 high school children, there were *3 abnormalities, or 5%.*[6] If one accepts the validity of this carefully selected control series, clinical findings in the literature demonstrating much higher incidence of EEG abnormalities in the populations studied cannot be ignored.

Another source of confusion is the use of phenobarbital and diphenylhydantoin (Dilantin) in treating patients who have EEG abnormalities, and finding no improvement in their behavior. The conclusion is then drawn that the EEG abnormalities have no meaning. But phenobarbital controls mainly grand mal manifestations, and diphenylhydantoin is frequently less effective than other medications when used for subconvulsive disorders. Thus, a wrong conclusion is being drawn about the EEG itself.

A further source of confusion lies in the technical limitations of the EEG itself. Because most abnormalities appear in the sleep state, an EEG in waking state only is quite inadequate. Yet, some studies use only the waking EEG. The EEG may be negative even in the presence of proved macroscopic organic brain disease or proved epilepsy. The conventional EEG taps only the outer convexity of the cerebrum, and only the outer centimeter or so. By using electrodes implanted in the deeper brain substance, investigators have shown that seizure activity (and accompanying behavioral disturbances) may occur at deeper levels, while surface electrodes reveal absolutely nothing unusual.[7]

Thus, the abnormalities shown up by the EEG are only *minimal* indicators of disturbed physiology, and a negative EEG cannot be presumed to prove the absence of organic brain disease.

Still, with all the uncertainties I have mentioned, tantalizing bits of evidence crop up which have led researchers to pursue the link between organic brain disease and violence. One might mention Jack Ruby, who shot Lee Harvey Oswald. He had a long history of erratic, impulsive and violent behavior. His EEG showed a marked psychomotor-variant dysrhythmia. Or Whitman, who picked off a dozen victims with a rifle from a tower at the University of Texas. He had a brain stem glioma.

The key concept in the relationship of organic brain disease to behavior is the notion of *dyscontrol,* described by Menninger.[8] It consists of varying degrees of disturbance in organization, failure in coping, escape of disruptive impulses, disruption of orderly thought processes and confusion.

Now it is known that in the brain the majority of messages are involved in inhibition, and only a small minority in facilitation. It is probable that when some lesion or dysfunction affects the brain, it will affect the inhibitory messages more than the facilitating, and if the inhibitions fail, the result would be some degree of dyscontrol.

From this follows another concept: one would expect to find more organic brain disease among those who commit sudden, impulsive acts of violence, than among those who coolly plan and execute such acts.

The most common organic brain disease, though a temporary one, is alcoholic intoxication. Half of all murders, suicides, and fatal automobile accidents are committed under the influence of alcohol.

Marinacci believes that alcohol does more than intoxicate, that in a susceptible person it facilitates temporal lobe epileptoid states.[9] He distinguishes between the person who gets drunk and bothers no one and the person who gets violent, sometimes even before he really gets intoxicated. He demonstrated that in a group of persons who had committed crimes of violence, that there were many with an abnormal EEG, especially temporal lobe abnormalities. He then retested those with a negative EEG by activation with alcohol, and found that in a considerable portion, this activation did indeed bring out temporal lobe dysrhythmia. Sometimes the activation would produce a rage reaction in the EEG laboratory.

It is clear that alcohol, whether by intoxication or by facilitating preexisting brain disease (pathologic intoxication) creates a condition in which violence is much more common than when the brain is in the normal state.

Epilepsy is also implicated in violence, though certainly not every epileptic is violent. It must be remembered that the epileptic seizure is only one manifestation of an underlying cerebral disorder. Even when seizures are absent, there may be dysrhythmias which affect cerebral functioning. Hill and Pond found that in 100 persons on trial for murder, there were 18 epileptics.[10] This is over 30 times the incidence in the general population. Blackman described 29 persons who committed sudden, impulsive murders; five had gross organic disease.[11] Fenton described a 52-year old man who killed his wife in a sudden rage; this happened shortly after his first akinetic epileptic seizure.[12]

Some studies show that persons who commit violence come from a background associated with broken homes and violence, but Weiss, in describing a number of murders, found that the sudden-impulsive murderers came from intact homes where violence was absent.[13] Bender found that 10 of 15 children who committed murder had an abnormal EEG, and three of these had developed clinical symptoms of epilepsy around the time of the murder.[14] Satten et al, described two of four murderers as having organic brain disease and a lifelong pattern of losing control.[15] In his cases, there was violence in the home as well.

In Illinois, a study at the St. Charles School for Boys, an institution for delinquent boys, demonstrated 25 per cent EEG abnormalities in an institution-wide sample, and 50 per cent abnormalities in a sample suspected of having a dysrhythmia by virtue of impulsiveness and dyscontrol in their history.[16]

In England, Stafford-Clark found that of 64 sudden-impulsive murderers, 70 per cent had an abnormal EEG. Of the 64, there were 27 in which the murder made some "sense," in that there was an understandable motivation, such as a husband finding his wife in bed with another man; of these 27, five had an abnormal EEG. Of "unmotivated" or "senseless" murderers, 15 out of 23 had an abnormal EEG.[17] Easson described eight boys who had murderously assaulted; seven had signs of organic brain disease.[18]

The discovery of XYY chromosomal abnormalities in some men raises interesting questions about its significance in behavior.[19] In one study of prisoners, XYY abnormality was found in one of 30, an incidence 10 times the general population.[20]

Violence often accompanies senile brain disease. I could find no statistics, but my clinical experience indicates this is not at all uncommon, and only physical feebleness keeps it from becoming a serious problem.

In children there is extremely high correlation between violence or aggressive behavior and organic brain disease. It is not uncommon to find a hyper-aggressive child in a family of several normal children, and to find neurologic abnormalities only in this one child. In children, it is much easier to detect "soft" neurologic signs, EEG abnormalities, and organic indicators on psychological tests, than in adults.

Turning now to my own experience: in 2,000 adult patients seen consecutively in private and clinic practice, there were 12 patients, all men, whose behavior seemed indicative of dyscontrol in the absence of psychosis. Of these, 10 had no background of violence in their parental home. All 12 had come to treatment under duress from the court or from family pressure. None had neurologic signs, but 11 had EEG abnormalities.

In all 12, anticonvulsants and other medications were prescribed. Initially, they appeared to improve, but sooner or later all were lost to follow-up, so no firm conclusions can be drawn.

A typical case is a 32-year old man who periodically would go on rampages against his wife, usually with minimal provocation. He agreed to see me only after his wife had threatened to leave. This man had paroxysmal bursts of 6/second spike-like waves throughout the occipital cortex, awake and asleep. He took methsuximide for about a year with no further outbreaks. Then, there was another phone call from his wife. He had stopped his medication and was back to tearing up the house. Unfortunately, these patients do not lend themselves to double-blind studies.

Just recently I was able to do a controlled study on a patient with pathologic intoxication. Even on small amounts of alcohol, he became violent with his wife; later there was total amnesia. On imipramine, he still had foggy spells under alcohol and acted peculiarly and irrationally, but not aggressively, whereas without imipramine, the violence returned.

In children, Wilson and I have been able to collect 1,000 consecutive cases referred to a child guidance center, all of whom were given psychiatric, neurologic and EEG examination, and about half of whom had psychological testing as well (retarded children were excluded).[21] Of the 1,000 children, 55 per cent had EEG abnormalities. Very few had "hard" neurologic signs. There was a high correlation between EEG abnormalities or other evidence of organic brain disease and tendencies to aggression and violence.

In many families, there was no evidence of significant psychopathology. A good example is Jimmy, whom we saw at age 9 because of serious rage reactions and aggressiveness leading to threatened expulsion from school. He was one of nine children, and the only one who had any behavior problems. In fact, the other children were considered outstanding in the community and at school. Jimmy had an identical twin, Johnny, who was considered a "model child." Jimmy's EEG showed left temporal spikes; Johnny's was negative. On methsuximide, Jimmy became an entirely different boy, a "model child" like his twin. When medication was omitted for a short time, he reverted to his old self by the third day. One could speculate what would have happened to him if he had continued to be "the black sheep" and get into trouble.

In Billy's case, the family background is quite different, but the same principle is illustrated. He was such a "monster" in kindergarten—pushing, shoving, knocking other children down—that he was expelled. He was one of a family of four boys and one girl. All four boys turned out to have abnormal EEG's and symptoms of minimal brain dysfunction, but the brothers' difficulties were not so severe as Billy's. Billy's father could not stand him and would ·

beat him up regularly. With dextroamphetamine, and a special class in school, his behavior problem simply disappeared despite his father's continued violence toward him. Academically he did unusually well. His IQ in kindergarten was 83; 8 months later it was 111, and 4 years later, 127. His father became less antagonistic to Billy, undoubtedly in response to Billy's changed behavior.

Ben illustrates the same principle in the opposite way. He was 13 when first referred to a psychiatrist. He had been repeatedly beaten up by his father, almost to the point of being killed. He was violent at home, a disciplinary problem in school, a slow learner (verbal IQ, 87; performance IQ, 113). His father had also been quick-tempered and had a history much like Ben's. He was harsh with his family, but would beat up only Ben. The father "tried to do the right thing" and was upset about getting into rages, one of which was described by a social worker as "suddenly becoming white as a sheet and running around the house like crazy."

Ben's EEG showed 14-6/second positive spikes; his father's showed positives spike and 6/second wave dysrhythmia. Medication was prescribed for both, but intervention came too late. Neither would take his medication. Mother divorced father. Ben was arrested for theft and is now committed to the Illinois Youth Commission.

In summary, there is a large body of evidence pointing to an association between organic brain disease, as defined in modern terms, and violence, particularly of the sudden-impulsive kind. The key concept is: organic brain disease→dyscontrol under minimal stimulation→potential for violence. The practical implications lie in the possibility of treating the disease by medication, thus preventing dyscontrol and violence. In children, this has been well-documented; medication is often extremely effective. In adults, not enough data have been accumulated to warrant definitive conclusions, but there is a reasonable possibility that here too the proper medication may be effective in reducing violence.

REFERENCES

1. Lombroso, C. T., et al: Neurology 16:1152, 1966.
2. Demerdash, A., et al: Develop Med Child Neurol 10:309, 1968.
3. Kellaway, P., et al: J Pediat 55:582, 1959.
4. Gibbs, F. A., and Gibbs, E. L.: Atlas of Electroencephalography, Vol. 3, Cambridge, Mass., Addison-Wesley Publ. Co., 1964.
5. Metcalf, D. R.: Electroenceph Clin Neurophysiol 15:161, 1963.
6. Wilson, W. C.: Personal Communication.
7. Ervin, F. R.: Presented at the Midwest Regional Conference on Violence and Aggression, Nov. 1968.
8. Menninger, K.: The Vital Balance, New York, The Viking Press, 1963.
9. Marinacci, A. A.: Bull Los Angeles Neurol Soc 28:241, 1963.
10. Hll, D., and Pond, D. A.: J Ment Sci 98:23, 1952.
11. Blackman, N., et al: Arch Gen Psychiat 8:289, 1963.
12. Fenton, G. W., and Udwin, E. L.: Brit J Psychiat 111:304, 1965.
13. Weiss, J.M.A., et al: Arch Gen Psychiat 2:669, 1960.

14. Bender, L.: Amer J Psychiat 116:510, 1959.
15. Satten, J., et al: Amer J Psychiat 117:48, 1960.
16. Personal Communication.
17. Stafford-Clark, D., and Taylor, F. H.: J Neurol Neurosurg Psychiat 12:325, 1949.
18. Easson, W. M., and Steinhilber, R. M.: Arch Gen Psychiat 4:1, 1967.
19. Marinello, M. J., et al: JAMA 208:321, 1969.
20. Jacobs, P. A., et al: Nature 208:1351, 1965.
21. Wilson, W. C., and Gross, M. D. *Unpublished Data.*

HOMICIDE IN ADOLESCENTS: FANTASY AND DEED

Michael G. Kalogerakis, M.D.

In nearly 10 years of work with adolescent patients admitted to Bellevue Psychiatric Hospital, I have examined large numbers of boys with problems of aggression. The male adolescent ward admits an average of 200 patients annually. These are boys aged 12 through 15 drawn largely from the lower socio-economic sections of New York. Perhaps all of them are struggling with aggressive thoughts of a conscious or unconscious order. A smaller proportion are contending with aggressive impulses of a destructive nature. Yet only a small number act behaviorally on such impulses and of these a rare few do so in a violent and dangerous fashion.

It is the last group I wish to discuss because they are, despite their relative unimportance numerically, the segment of the psychopathological continuum causing the greatest concern to society.

Beyond the sometimes thorny problems of diagnosis, we are continually confronted, on an adolescent psychiatric service, with the issue of prognosis. In fact, prediction, upon which all questions of management and disposition depend, is probably the most pressing problem that we have as we approach the study of violence in individuals. We are in desperate need of methods for sorting out from the many troubled individuals in our society those who will be the murderers in tomorrow's headlines.

Assaultive individuals, arsonists and rapists, who represent equally important dangers, need to be distinguished from those posing less serious threats. It is by no means certain that this is possible in the majority of instances. However, if, from the many individuals who come to our attention before they have committed their first serious offense, even a few can be picked out, a significant reduction in violent crime might result.

Dr. Kalogerakis is assistant clinical professor of psychiatry at New York University Medical Center, New York, New York.

Because a very large number of adult murderers have a history of anti-social behavior or serious emotional disturbance dating back to adolescence or earlier, that phase of development becomes the logical point at which to concentrate efforts to identify and treat the potentially dangerous person.

I shall present two cases, both 15-year-old boys admitted to Bellevue Psychiatric Hospital who had been preoccupied for some time with the idea of committing murder. In the first boy, the act was finally consummated in the double murder of his maternal grandmother and her paramour. The other patient was admitted because of persistent and elaborate thoughts of murdering his parents and two sisters following the reading of Truman Capote's *In Cold Blood*.

Case No. 1

Peter, the first boy, had a childhood filled with rejection, separation, abuse and disorganization. He was the only child born to an Irish-American mother, probably out-of-wedlock. He never knew his father, who had apparently been jailed for bank robbery about the time of the boy's birth. When Peter was about three the mother married a career soldier who demanded strict discipline at home and administered frequent and, according to the patient, merciless beatings.

Punishment sometimes consisted of being locked in the closet. The step-father openly admitted disliking children and Peter in particular. Finally, the mother and stepfather moved to Texas leaving Peter in New York with his grandmother. This initiated a series of moves in which the boy lived alternately with his mother and grandmother, invariably being sent to his grandmother when his mother or stepfather were fed up with him.

Each of his first four years of school was disrupted by these moves. By the fourth grade he had behavior and learning problems. He was absent for more than half the year, failed all his subjects and was not promoted. Truancy soon became a way of life for him. He grew to hate and fear his stepfather and fared no better with his grandmother, but somehow maintained the illusion that his mother still loved him and was not to blame for his misfortune, because she was ill, apparently of diabetes.

There is some indication that she infantilized and probably overstimulated him when he was living with her. He cut school to stay with her when she was not feeling well. He remembers being jealous when his friends would talk to her. He apparently slept in the same bed with either mother or grandmother until a late age (9 to 10).

Early signs of disturbance included sadistic treatment of animals: he would dismember flies, birds and lizards. He once killed a cat with a rock and his bare hands, then set it afire. He remembered feeling joyous excitement while doing this. Violence filled his childhood in other ways: he described how his grandfather burned to death in a fire. He was certain the fire was set by his grandmother while her husband was asleep.

He recalled many battles between his mother and grandmother, including one in which his mother was choking the older woman who apparently had been haranguing her about the boy's father. When the grandmother remarried, the step-grandfather joined in abusing the boy.

Chaotic sexuality also characterized his home life. He very often saw intercourse between the adults in his family and once surprised his mother and *step-grandfather* in the basement, an incident he brought up to his mother many times afterwards. This and other instances of infidelity finally caused the grandmother to throw out her second husband.

By the time Peter reached adolescence he was living more regularly with his grandmother. He was a depressed, nervous youngster whose shyness and fearfulness brought expressions of hostility from his schoolmates. Prejudice against Negroes and Puerto Ricans had been instilled in him by his mother in the South and did not facilitate adjustment in an integrated New York public school.

At home he was exploited by his grandmother who ran a rooming house. Peter was responsible for cleaning it without remuneration. The boy subsequently complained bitterly that he even had to beg for clothing. She was deeply preoccupied with the Catholic religion to a fanatical degree, as Peter saw it. In addition, her violent outbursts, which were sometimes directed at her bachelor son who lived with them (they often threatened to kill one another), and sometimes at Peter, often took a cruel and humiliating turn. Once she threw hot water at Peter and sprayed insecticide in his face. Another time she cut his wrists as he tried to wrestle a knife away from her. In this atmosphere Peter thought often of suicide.

The grandmother finally became concerned enough about his nervousness to take him to a psychiatric clinic, where she was told to let up on him. This led to a temporary improvement before the grandmother renewed her usual manner of dealing with the boy. Then matters became worse. Peter's truancy finally led to Juvenile Term Court. He was then 14, and was remanded for further psychiatric evaluation after the school had attempted unsuccessfully to solve the problem. The boy was then admitted to a state hospital.

Less than two months later, his grandmother signed him out, apparently convinced he was all right and probably in need of his services at home. Peter had been experiencing auditory hallucinations at that time. However he withheld this information so as not to be kept in the hospital.

Back in the community, Peter again experienced serious difficulty. His truancy continued and when he went to school he was the subject of ridicule because of his odd appearance. He wore cowboy boots and other western-style clothing, shook noticeably, and was labeled a junkie by schoolmates. He got into many fights, usually with Negroes, was robbed and beaten up on several occasions, and became increasingly concerned that he would be knifed in the back. At this time he wrote to his mother in Texas asking for a gun. *This was sent to him together with a supply of ammunition.*

He carried his gun with him at all times, frequently thinking of suicide. The act that brought him to our attention occurred several months later, on

Christmas eve. Peter was with a friend and had been sent out by his grandmother to get some pizza. When they returned, he was severely upbraided by his grandmother and her boyfriend for failing to get the right kind.

As insults poured forth, the boy felt humiliated and distraught. He thought of shooting himself with the gun he was carrying, but instead turned it first on the grandmother's boyfriend, killing him instantly, and then on her, reloading and emptying it on the dying woman as she pleaded for a doctor. He then shot his own dog, apparently because it was barking.

Peter's predominant feeling immediately after the crime was one of tremendous relief: she no longer would be able to nag and harass him. He bitterly recalled how she had broken his spirit in the year preceding the murder, to the extent that he had become detached and no longer able to enjoy things. He had difficulty sleeping and avoided relationships.

He said: "The old witch thought she would never die." He rationalized: "I did her a favor; she was crazy and would have ended up suffering in a state hospital." (She had in fact been hospitalized at Bellevue several years before). He indicated that now he could see his stepfather and not be afraid any more. Also he said he didn't feel like killing himself any more.

Clinically, he was a pathetic figure to behold—asthenic, submissive in general demeanor, depressed, crushed. He cooperated fully with the staff, described auditory hallucinations, and displayed psychotic reality testing, by wondering whether his gun would be returned.

In fact he became obsessively preoccupied with guns of all kinds and hoped to go to Viet Nam or Africa some day where he could use a gun freely. He was sorry he would now never be able to be a policeman, which had been his desire for some time.

Case No. 2

Alfonso, the second patient, was also 15 on admission. His history contrasts sharply with Peter's. He came from an intact professional family. He was of superior intelligence and was doing very well in a select high school. He always had been quite withdrawn, even schizoid, and suffered from severe acne. There were none of the behavior problems that marked Peter's life from an early age.

The stresses in Alfonso's life were characteristically middle-class-professional, despite living in apartment developments in ghetto areas. His father, a Puerto Rican raised in a broken disorganized home, married out of his culture, taking an Austrian-born Jew as his wife. He set high goals for himself and labored many years, attending college at night. He finally completed the requirements for becoming a laboratory technician two or three years before Alfonso's admission to the hospital.

He set equally demanding scholastic standards for his children. Alfonso and his older sister were able to meet these standards, but the third-born, a girl, was not doing as well. Alfonso's relationship with his father consisted largely of an endless string of arguments or debates on many different issues which the boy always felt he lost. He generally felt put down by his father in these contests and tried desperately to sharpen his intellectual skills.

He was not involved in sports, and participated in very little shared recreational activity. Alfonso's father, usually reserved and controlled, could also be explosive and represented a veritable powder keg to the boy.

The mother, an intelligent and concerned woman who had no college education or special training, came to the United States at the age of 17 after her parents died in concentration camps. Her influence in the boy's life is not as clear as the father's but there is evidence that she avoided any physical contact because "it might make him a sissy," and, instead assumed the role of protecting him from the father. In one notable instance, when she found Alfonso, then 11, with his exposed 8-year-old sister in the bedroom, she did not relate the incident to her husband, but told him only that Alfonso was having sexual dreams and seemed to be otherwise preoccupied with sexual matters. This led the father to discuss masturbation with the boy.

The effect of this discussion is open to question, because Alfonso became regularly involved sexually with his sister for the next few years. Digital masturbation was the usual form of contact.

From an early age, this boy showed a predilection for fantasy and little interest in interpersonal contact. He was shy, friendless, and played with his teddy bears into adolescence. He called one bear Julius Caesar and gave the others German names with an aristocratic ring, a significant choice in the light of his mother's experiences during the Nazi era.

When he was only 5, he devised a game which he played by himself and told no one about. It consisted of making paper models which invariably became police cars and other props for a "cops and robbers" game. In this play, police usually converged from all directions on an urban intersection where a crime had been committed.

"It was like a little world of my own which I was commanding. I was powerful in my own world, powerless in the real world. Whenever I finished a game I would destroy everything—it seemed senseless to do this."

Power and control, admixed with aggression in various forms, remained Alfonso's predominant preoccupations. In his mind he developed a scheme for world government in which he would rule. Alternately he assumed the role of the just though powerful ruler, then that of the criminal flouting authority, expressing another kind of power.

For two or three years prior to admission he had avidly read books on homicide. Some eight months before he came to our attention, his father gave him a copy of *In Cold Blood*. He became fascinated with the story, and identified strongly with one of the two protagonists, Perry. In the ensuing months, he re-read the book several times and at some point decided that he must do as Perry did, i.e., plan to kill a family of four, in this case his own. To assure that he would than receive the electric chair (under the modified N.Y. State law governing capital punishment), he would also have to kill a policeman.

His basic intention was to kill his father. He felt humiliated by him, recalling that when he was 4 or 5 and had resumed wetting the bed, his father beat him and made him stand outside his room as punishment. The desire to kill the others was explained as a wish not to have them suffer as a result of the father's death.

In the months when Alfonso was developing these thoughts, there were visible changes in him. He withdrew more than ever, sent hours alone in his room, and was tense and irritable at mealtimes. He finally confided his thoughts to his younger sister. They were apparently dismissed lightly at first by parents who could not believe so much violence could exist in their son.

When conflict over his murderous thoughts and his continuing sexual involvement with his sister became unbearable, Alfonso finally requested help and was in fact started in psychotherapy at a university guidance center. As the full extent of Alfonso's feelings became apparent to the psychologist who was treating him, and as the impulse to kill began to take on an irresistible character—it was for a time focussed on a senior in school who had called him "swollen-nose"—hospitalization was considered.

Only when he began to carry a scalpel and threatened his father was the latter able to recognize the seriousness of his son's disturbance and agree to hospitalization. By then a true crisis had developed so that for the first time the boy's academic performance was affected and he began to misbehave in school. He damaged some property and threatened an assistant principal. He reached a point where he refused to remain in the apartment because he was afraid his father would kill him.

He was acutely psychotic on admission, although he was not hallucinating and was not truly delusional. His condition improved over the next several weeks with the aid of medication and psychotherapy. Despite a stormy course marked by several suicide attempts and an intense and disturbing emotional involvement with one of the nurses, he became well enough to return to his home and to school while continuing intensive psychotherapy. The fantasies of committing murder had subsided but they had not disappeared. They had in part been replaced by romantic daydreams about his nurse.

Comment

What accounts for Peter translating his fantasy into deed, and what accounts for Alfonso *not* acting upon his homicidal impulses? (At the time of our examination, it was our impression that there had been ample reason to fear the homicidal outcome in the case of Peter, but we felt reasonably sure Alfonso would not act upon his impulses).

Both represent examples of familiar adolescent personality types. Though both boys were diagnosed schizophrenic, Peter is representative of the so-called "acting out" youngster. Alfonso's development showed many of the features we find in the obsessional personality.

In both boys, family experiences engendered feelings of resentment to the point of bitterness, as well as feelings of worthlessness and impotence. An important difference appears, however, in the differing styles of *expression* of such feelings, as set by the parents and parent surrogates. Blatant, hostile rejection together with physical brutality characterized Peter's experience, whereas Alfonso was the victim of more covert rejection and milder punitive action.

It would appear that for Peter, the *entire* home environment was hostile, despite his desperate efforts to rationalize his mother's actions and regard her as the only one who cared. She was obviously more solicitous of her husband than she was concerned with her son's development.

Alfonso, on the other hand, had a mother who cared and showed it. Murder was regularly threatened and possibly even committed by the adults in Peter's life. Such a history was lacking in Alfonso's case. Whether the process involves imitation or identification (with the aggressor) or a combination of these and other factors is not clear and requires careful study.

The simple fact that the significant adult figures in one boy's life are openly saying "Killing is O.K.—I might even do it myself", while the others are at least paying lip service to the traditional prohibitions against killing, though possibly transmitting something quite different unconsciously (e.g. Alfonso's father's gift of "In Cold Blood"), may constitute a most important difference.

To counteract the hostility-producing forces in Alfonso's situation there were constructive forces, chiefly in the emphasis which was placed on education and achievement. Alfonso's scholastic excellence gave him a sense of self-esteem which, however restricted it may have been, had no corollary in Peter's life. The total lack of any feeling of self-worth in the latter was a major source of depression and hopelessness, and ultimately led to serious suicidal propensities.

I believe this to be an ominous development in the history of a person already beset with destructive urges: once he no longer cares about his own life, anyone else's life is cheap. It is important in this regard to distinguish the true suicidal wish from the suicidal gesture whose aim is not death but a manipulation of, or impact on, some particular person. (This was the case with Alfonso on the ward, when he sought to impress our nurse with the strength of his feelings for her).

Quite early in their lives, the boys had taken separate pathways. While Alfonso became engrossed in creative play with his paper models, Peter already was involved in the sadistic treatment and killing of animals. This finding, though it does not necessarily herald a malignant personality development, is frequently seen in the early histories of murderers and other violent individuals. Though Peter later became a lover of pets, this early transgression clearly expressed a disregard for the importance of life.

It is probably quite significant that at the time he shot his grandmother, he also shot his dog. Though from the very beginning neither boy was taught or allowed an appropriate way to express anger, Alfonso sought to express his anger in fantasy and play. Peter expressed anger by injuring living creatures. It is generally recognized that once an existing, strongly held taboo is broken by a given individual—and this would apply not only to killing but also to incest, striking one's parent, etc.—the barrier no longer seems impenetrable and further transgressions will occur more readily.

To what extent these patients were the victims and, in the case of Peter, the executors of their parents' murderous wishes (as in a series of cases presented by Sargent)[1], is difficult to say, although the evidence that this was a powerful factor in Peter's life is very compelling. It is hard to imagine that a mother would give a revolver to a disturbed 15-year-old boy living unhappily with a grandmother she herself found intolerable, unless some unconscious death wish were present.

A further area of difference between the two boys is that Peter's struggle was largely with external forces: that is with *real* as opposed to fantasied threats, which had to be handled by direct interaction with others. Alfonso, on the other hand, was coping with few outside dangers and suffered largely from intrapsychic conflicts which required little actual involvement with others and could be worked out at a fantasy level. In concrete terms he did not arm himself with a weapon to fend off possible attackers, as did Peter.

One might wonder why a boy such as Peter faced with the unlivable situation he was in, did not run away as other children do. The answer probably lies in the fact that even with such overwhelming rejection, the child still held on to the fantasy that somehow everything might work out and that his needs for love and nurturance would finally be met. There was strong evidence of a neurotic ambivalence with erotic components in the dream Peter had the night after the murder: he was having sexual intercourse with a girl when her parents came home; he couldn't come to climax, got angry and shot her.

In his associations to the dream he said that the room looked like his grandmother's bedroom. Also, he reported experiencing an erection at the time of the actual shooting, though he denied associated sexual feelings. This is reminiscent of the experience described by some arsonists and requires careful investigation. In forensic psychiatry, the admixture of violence and sexuality has been accurately underscored as particularly dangerous.

A final note of interest concerning the two patients is that both had expressed desires to be policemen or other law enforcement officers. This appears to be an attempt to cope with their feelings of total impotence and physical vulnerability in a socially acceptable manner, while affording themselves the opportunity of finally taking out their hostility on some hapless criminal.

Evaluating Potential for Violence

At this point, I should like to address myself in a more general way to the issue of clinically evaluating the potential for dangerous acts by the mentally ill. This was the subject of a panel at the American Psychiatric Association meetings in 1965,[2] which contributed much of what follows but left numerous questions unanswered. My emphasis will be on the adolescent patient, but applicability to adults should be self-evident.

In attempting to assess the potential for dangerous actions in a given individual, three factors must be carefully evaluated:

(1) *The impulses*—their nature and strength.

(2) *The controls*—including judgment, frustration tolerance, moral and ethical principles.

(3) *The expected life situation*—what *real* pressures, influences and contacts will the individual be facing on return to the community?

Traditionally, anamnestic data provide answers to all three areas but these are at best partial. A careful history of past behavior should go beyond establishing the presence of aggressive impulses, since these are common and varied in the adolescent population. One needs to know what specific aggressive feelings, e.g., anger, hostility, rage, the wish to destroy objects or set fire, murderous impulses, etc., are stored up, and what stimuli, internal as well as external, are sufficient to trigger such feelings.

Their intensity under different conditions of stress is important. Observation of behavior on a psychiatric ward, particularly if it includes peers, is valuable and mandatory when there is reason to believe that anamnestic material is being withheld or is incomplete.

Beyond behavior, and here we must keep in mind the murderer who has never displayed any significant aggression previously, we must use whatever techniques are available to get at the fantasies, dreams and thoughts of the individual, both conscious and unconscious.

There is probably no substitute here for the skillful clinical interview, and adolescents are notoriously reticent about sharing their thoughts. In cases, however, which yield little or nothing via the interview approach, the projective techniques of the clinical psychologist are often helpful.

It is on the matter of controls that diagnostic considerations become important. Although not all schizophrenics are struggling with dangerously aggressive impulses, it is probably safe to say that all have a reduced capacity to control such urges when they do occur, at least in the acute phases of their illness. The same may be said for the organically brain damaged or epileptic patient.

The true sociopath, who is unable to care about the well-being of another human being, obviously lacks the braking mechanisms that may serve to deter another person with equally strong destructive impulses. I should like to stress, however, that even in the sociopath, the important defect is not usually in superego functions in the form of poor values and principles as is often maintained, (*vide* "superego lacunae concept" of A. Johnson).[3] The defect is in ego functions such as judgment and frustration tolerance.

In this respect, I am in complete agreement with Sargent.[1] Further, it is apparent that anything which interferes with the capacity to exercise sound judgment in a given situation, notably, drinking and drug abuse, significantly increases the risk posed by the aggressive individual.

Finally, the situational factors likely to be encountered by the individual may have a threefold effect in augmenting danger: contact with a nagging, harassing grandmother, as in Peter's case, may acutely aggravate the simmering violent feelings. Prodding by fellow gang members may weaken tenuous controls. Frequenting bars or associating with criminal elements may produce an inescapable situation which begets violence.

I will close by summing up much of the above in a series of questions for use by the examining physician faced with the task of evaluating the potential for dangerous actions by an emotionally disturbed adolescent. Although the questions have been carefully drawn from extensive work with adolescents at Bellevue, they do not at this juncture purport to be either complete or adequate.

They should alert the examiner to important areas for further exploration in a given patient. Their reliability must await the completion of predictive studies now in progress. They draw heavily upon the work of previous authors, notably Bychowski,[4, 5] Satten et al[6] and others, but hopefully suggest additional areas of emphasis and exploration.

(1) Have the life experiences been such as to create resentment and bitterness?

(2) Is he consciously aware of having such feelings?

(3) Has he found effective (non-destructive) ways of expressing these feelings?

(4) Does he seem to have regard for himself as a person?

(5) Does he seem to have regard for other people—their well-being, their life?

(6) Is there a source of self-esteem in his current life accompanied by a sense that his efforts are appreciated by a significant person? Good performance in school or at work, and a sense of being liked or loved are important.

(7) Has he been and is he currently under the influence of a significant figure (e.g. family member, gang member) who himself has murderous impulses?

(8) Is he often exposed to situations in which dangerous provocation is likely to occur?

(9) Is there evidence that demands or pressure on the patient have been increasing of late? Conversely, is there evidence of recent deterioration in the patient's ability to cope with life's tasks and pressures and/or his aggressive impulses?

(10) Is there meaningful contact with people?

(11) When aggressive feelings have built up to the breaking point in the past, has he alerted others, or dropped hints? This is frequently the case with the suicidal patient and probably occurs more commonly than generally believed in the homicidal individual as well.[6]

REFERENCES

1. Sargent, D.: *Children Who Kill*—A Family Conspiracy, Social Work, 1962.

2. Rappeport, J. R.: *The Clinical Evaluation of the Dangerousness of the Mentally Ill*, C. C. Thomas, Springfield, Ill., 1967.
3. Johnson, A. M.: *Sanctions for Superego Lacunae of Adolescents* in Searchlights on Delinquency, Eissler, K. R., editor, International Universities Press, Inc., 1949.
4. Bychowski, G.: In Rappeport, above.
5. Bychowski, G.: *Evil in Man,* Grune & Stratton, New York, 1968.
6. Satten, J., Menninger, K., Rosen, I., and Mayman, M.: Amer J Psychiat 117, 1960.

THE LETHAL SITUATION:
TRANSMISSION OF URGE TO
KILL FROM PARENT TO CHILD

Douglas A. Sargent, M.D.

Introduction:

Recently, tragic events in the United States have forced us to take a hard, second look at a neglected topic: murder. The assassination of three towering figures, together with a barrage of civil rights murders, seems to have made the study of murderers a matter of pressing concern. But we must face the fact that the scientific study of murder is still in its infancy. Far from being able to predict from firm data who will kill and who will not kill, we have not advanced beyond the level of descriptive study. Attempts to remedy this deficit could start with a series of questions outlining the areas needing further study. One question we might ask now is: *What do we know of the context in which murder becomes possible?*

Let us call this context the *lethal situation*. For descriptive purposes, let us define the *lethal situation* as the combination of psychological and social circumstances which must obtain in order for murder to take place, and without which a murder is unlikely to occur. In addition to the elements which are usually considered relevant, such as the motive, the opportunity, and the availability of a lethal weapon, there are other elements, interpersonal and social ones, which also must be present before a lethal situation can be said to exist.

Following is a descriptive study of two killings which were committed by young children. No claims are made for statistical significance or scientific controls. Instead this study will focus on the development of the lethal situation, which is one facet of the act of murder that may be susceptible to external influence. The elements comprising the lethal situation will be described and some conclusions about the possibility of prevention will be discussed.

Dr. Sargent is professor and chairman of the Department of Psychiatry at the College of Osteopathic Medicine, Michigan State University.

I Myth vs. Reality:

The act of murder interests everyone. Looking at the ranks of paperback novels in any airline terminal, it is obvious that, next to love, murder is the most popular of all literary themes. Perhaps because it lulls guilt feelings about our own hidden impulses, the search for the unknown murderer, his apprehension and his punishment, is highly absorbing to us. The relief we experience through externalizing our own unconscious murderous impulses may explain the well-known soporific effect of the murder mystery.

Murder is an intensely human act, ordinarily occurring in the context of close interpersonal relationships and involving motivations immediately understandable to all. Man's role as killer is at least as ancient as are his more gentle accomplishments: the archeological evidence of his victims and his weapons bears impressive testimony to this fact.[1] The ubiquitous nature of the urge to kill allows us to empathize with the killer, even while we deplore his act, devise his punishment and mourn his victim. These conflicting emotions hamper scientific efforts to apply rational methods to the prevention of murder.

As a form of destructive human behavior, murder would seem to merit at least as much study as suicide. Yet scientific papers about suicide far outnumber papers about homicide. We are much less sanguine about the possibility of preventing homicide than we are about preventing suicide. This pessimistic attitude is not supported by rational argument, but rests on rumor, myth and mystical beliefs. The fact is that murderers usually act from perfectly comprehensible motives and in predictable ways, giving warning of their intent. They often use conventional weapons, confess their guilt, stoically accept or even seek their punishment, which, if it is not forthcoming, they may inflict upon themselves through suicide.

II The Killers:

Children who kill form a class of murderers whose dynamics are especially transparent and available to study. In a previous publication,[2] I said:

> ... Sometimes the child who kills is acting as the unwitting lethal agent of an adult (usually a parent) who unconsciously prompts the child to kill so that he can vicariously enjoy the benefits of the act. There are two corollaries to this hypothesis: first, that the adult plays upon the latent currents of hostility the child feels toward the victim—hostility, which without the adult's provocation and the child's special susceptibility, probably would remain inoperative and under the control of the child's ego: and the second, that the child's susceptibility to, and readiness to act upon, the unconscious prompting of the adult rests upon the immaturity of the child's ego and the presence of a special emotional bond between the child and the adult.

After presenting case material and a discussion in support of these claims, I went on to suggest that:

> ... both the process by which a parent *selects a particular child as the agent* of expression for his unconscious aggression and the *process of communication* of these impulses between child and parent, would seem to offer the investigator fruitful fields of study.

The following two cases are presented because they highlight the processes of selection and communication mentioned above. In each it is apparent that the motivation for the murder resided primarily in a parent, not in the child who committed the fatal act. What is of greater interest here, however, is the unusually clear evidence of the channels of *communication* between parent and child by which the fatal message was conveyed, an element essential to the *lethal situation*.

Case No. 1

Freddie, age 9, smothered his six-month-old half brother, Jack, when the baby's crying distracted him from watching a television murder story. Freddie had been left in charge of Jack and another half-brother, George, age 2, when their parents went out one evening. In accordance with his mother's instructions Freddie gave Jack a bottle. When it failed to quiet him, Freddie held a pillow over Jack's face until he was dead, then lay down in his parents' bed beside the body and fell asleep. He was still sleeping when his parents returned.

Freddie's step-father attempted, in vain, to resuscitate the baby. Freddie later said that his mother shook him awake and screamed at him, "Why didn't you kill George instead?" In an interview, Freddie's mother confirmed the question. Without apparent awareness of its peculiar nature, but, as though in explanation, she related some details of her own life from which the following story was pieced together:

At the age of 11 Freddie's mother was showing off a party dress her father had given her, when a jealous younger sister set it ablaze. Attracted by his older daughter's screams, the father rushed in from out of doors and smothered the flames. This rescue strongly impressed the girl who was saved. Shortly thereafter, the father, a drunkard who was often cruel to his family, deserted them, never to return. But from that time on, the rescued child, Freddie's mother, was preoccupied with fantasies in which she found her lost father and enticed him to come home. These fantasies continued, in one form or another into adult life, and were acted out in a variety of ways, one of which has particular interest for us.

When she was grown, Freddie's mother either married, or lived casually with, a series of men who treated her badly, then deserted her, leaving behind a variegated cluster of children whom she reared in a cruel, heedless fashion. These "bad fathers" played into her sadomasochistic family romance. The man who was her husband at the time of the killing was an apathetic ne'er-do-well, whom she supported. He competed openly with the children for her attention. In this home there also lived several "girls" whose profession attracted a stream of drunken men. Sometimes Freddie's mother also be-friended these men.

Freddie's mother claimed that a week before Freddie killed the baby she had a premonitory dream. In it, the house caught fire and a child died in the flames, despite her husband's attempts to revive it. In telling the dream, though, she misspoke herself and called her husband "my father." Because of the warning dream, she said, a death in the family was no surprise to her. She remembered also that, a few days before the killing, she solemnly warned Freddie that if an infant should become entangled in bedclothes, he might smother. She remembered that Freddie seemed amused by this idea. She was unable to explain why she had felt it necessary to give such a warning.

The misery of Freddie's life and of the lives of his legitimate half-siblings was only exceeded by that of the bastard, George, whom their mother "expected" Freddie to smother. This boy was neither loved nor tolerated. He was beaten by his mother more often than the other children were. Freddie disliked George, but also pitied him. He revealed that often people would forcibly interrupt his mother's savage beatings of George, warning her that she might kill him. (Yet no one took any effective steps to protect him!) But, Freddie was his mother's favorite. Although she turned over his care to strangers for the first two years of his life, she took him back to live with her when he was 2 because she "wanted him," which was more than the other children could claim.

His favored position, however, was a mixed blessing. His strange mother obliged Freddie to do housework and similar tasks which otherwise would have been hers. She treated Freddie as an equal rather than a child. There was little conversation between them. Neither of them thought this strange. His mother was also uncritical of the fact that when he was not doing her work he remained alone in his room, often watching the television set which she had bought for his sole use.

Freddie reported to the writer that, ever since he was 5, he had had an imaginary companion whom he described as follows: "I see the Bad Freddie in the other room when it's dark, out the window at night. He bees every place that I bees; he bees me."

Bad Freddie often gave orders. Once he told Freddie to jump off a high building, but Freddie did not obey. Freddie claimed that he smothered Jack by accident, but was upset because Bad Freddie whispered in his ear that he really had done it on purpose. Sometimes Bad Freddie took over Freddie's voice and made him swear or insult people. (This was impressively demonstrated for the writer during his examination of Freddie.)

Freddie said that he (too!) had a strange dream a day or two before Jack's death:

I was standing beside my house and I saw the girl across the street—she's my girlfriend—kissing some boys. I was Tarzan. I was jealous and I took her away from the boys and pushed her into my house through the side window. Then the house burned down. Maybe the baby burned. Maybe she burned. I'm not sure. I tried to get her out.

Freddie drew a picture of Tarzan, a strange hermaphrodite with a loin cloth and large, pendulous breasts which Freddie did not find inappropriate to a male.

Psychological and psychiatric study of Freddie and his mother showed that they were deeply entwined in a symbiotic relationship. They shared a common identity and a reservoir of id impulses which were loosely held in check by a poorly differentiated ego. Communication between mother and son flowed freely at a deep, empathic level. The apparent coincidence of their simultaneous dreams was only one aspect of their psychological fusion.

Within this relationship, Freddie often acted-out his mother's impulses as if he were an extension of her. The material suggests that this woman, whose emotional life was dominated by the wish to regain her lost father-rescuer, was driven repeatedly to place children in situations of danger in the unconscious hope that a rescuer-father would be attracted to her by their plight.

Her son, as the "Bad Freddie," acted this out for her, adding some motivation of his own (sibling rivalry.) His imaginary companion represented Freddie's attempt to maintain a degree of ego-integrity by splitting-off and disowning the bad impulses which were being imposed on him by his mother. Freddie's treatment in a mental hospital and ultimate placement with a foster family were accepted by his mother with stoic resignation, as if *his* removal and confinement constituted *her* punishment.

Case No. 2

Gertrude, age 7, decapitated her 6 year-old sister, Helen, with a single blast of her step-father's shotgun, which he had left loaded behind the headboard of his bed. While Gertrude later admitted she was angry at her sister, she was "only playing," and had no intention of killing her. Her father explained to the police that he kept the gun as protection against prowlers, and had forgotten to unload it when he left home that morning. The matter was dropped by the police.

Gertrude and her mother, however, told a different story. They claimed that the father could not have unloaded the gun that morning even if he had wanted to, because he had not come home. Instead, he had stayed out all night carousing, as he often did.

About a year before the shooting, shortly after the birth of a child, Gertrude's step-father became inordinately jealous of his wife, although she gave him no cause. He took to going out evenings to drink with the boys, leaving behind a loaded shotgun as a warning to his wife, should she be tempted to be unfaithful in his absence.

Six months later, he bought a hunting license and forced the girls, Gertrude and Helen, to set up targets for him to shoot at, ordering them to examine the holes of entry and exit made by the bullets. He told them to warn their mother that he was a good shot.

Three months thereafter he threw a meat cleaver at his wife, which narrowly missed her head and embedded itself in a door. He often beat her in front of the children and accused her of adultery. Once he instructed 3-year-old Richard to hit his mother between the eyes with a hair-brush, which Richard did, inflicting a cut. She passively accepted this abuse.

A month before the shooting, this deranged man held the shotgun to his wife's head, told her sister to get her black dress on, "because you're going to a funeral," and pulled the trigger on an empty chamber. He laughed at the fear and horror this "joke" evoked in the many adults and children who witnessed it.

Later, he shot his wife in the ankle with a blank charge, scorching her skin. He was amused by the children's frightened screams. In front of the other children, he often told Richard, his favorite child, to take the shotgun and shoot his mother.

Gertrude often was made to perform unusual personal services for her step-father. Because she was jealous of the preference her step-father showed for Richard, she was pleased to comply. She often fetched her step-father's gun for him when he played his "jokes." He taught her how to hold and aim the gun and often forced her to point it at her mother. But at other times this man pointedly ignored Gertrude because she was not his child. Gertrude was sensitive to these slights and often told her mother, "I wish Daddy would stop acting so funny and stay home with us."

Helen, the victim of the shooting, was openly hated by her father, who often whipped her without provocation. He justified this to his cringing family by claiming that he was punishing her because she resembled her namesake, his hated mother. A few days before Helen's death, her father attempted to whip both her and Gertrude because he suspected them of stealing the cross he had recently hung over his bed to protect him against his "enemies." He warned his wife, who tried to intervene, that if she ever attempted to leave him for another man she would be carried out in a box.

Gertrude's mother later explained her unusual, passive acceptance of this brutality by saying that she feared her husband, and that she had promised her mother on her death-bed never to leave him. This abused woman was weak, dependent, child-like, of limited intelligence and of a masochistic disposition. In her weakness, she was not able to defend herself, let alone protect her children against her husband's incomprehensible cruelty. (Nevertheless, she was able to leave her husband a week after Helen's funeral.)

Gertrude, who had been a bright, alert child and a good student until the shooting, was born out of wedlock and was raised by her maternal grandmother until she was 4 years old. At that time, she returned to live with her mother because her 15-year-old sister, who until that time had lived in the mother's home, put out an eye of another child in a fight. The Juvenile Court ordered the 15-year-old to leave her mother and live with the maternal grandmother, whose home was deemed a more fit place for a child. She and Gertrude traded places. Unfortunately, however, Gertrude proved to be no more impervious to the atmosphere of violence in her mother's home than her older sister had been.

This, then, was the psychological setting in which the homicide occurred: A fatherless child was transplanted, at an impressionable age, from the matriarchal home in which she had been raised to a household headed by a man. The paternal affection and care for which she always had longed was now available to her, but only under unusual and extreme circumstances. In order to win her step-father's love, Gertrude had to adopt his paranoid view that her mother was a traitor whom she should despise and even harm. In the competition for his favor, Gertrude had to excel as the handmaiden of his murderous jealousy.

Her immature ego and superego were unable to resist the intense and unremitting pressure of sadistic aggression to which she was continuously exposed. As the outsider who sought acceptance in the family, Gertrude may have been more susceptible than the other children were to a seduction into violence. At the same time, she entered the home as the replacement for an older girl whose violence had caused her removal, and she was the oldest and strongest of the remaining children. These forces probably played a part in her selection as the killer.

The spark that finally touched off the shooting was not discovered. Nevertheless, the atmosphere of explosive aggression in which Gertrude lived abounded in sparks. The victim selected by the child was, next to her mother, her father's favorite target for abuse. We may speculate that feelings of loyalty or affection caused Gertrude to deflect her father-triggered aggression away from her mother onto this secondary target, who was also a rival. (The dead child was the oldest legitimate child living in the home.)

It was evident that Gertrude, who had no concept of death and frequently had seen her mother threatened without serious harm, was neither able to anticipate nor to appreciate the grave consequences of her act. Realizing this, at the request of the psychiatric clinic, the Juvenile Court held an informal hearing at which Gertrude's blamelessness was impressed upon her. Several months of psychotherapy for Gertrude followed, accompanied by social casework assistance for her mother. The goal of this treatment was to help Gertrude handle the residue of confused emotions which remained after this dramatic experience. For a time these efforts seemed to be successful. However, the case was followed only for six months.

III Summary:

Two vignettes have been presented from lengthy studies of two children who killed siblings. The presentation of these complex cases has focused on the means by which the murderous wishes of adults were *communicated* to and acted upon by children. These "means" were subsumed under the term, the *lethal situation.*

In the first case, the message was conveyed in subtle tones over the private communication network which existed between a symbiotic mother-son pair. In the second case, the message was broadcast, in a blatant fashion, that violence was expected, that two targets were to be given priority, and that the reward of paternal esteem would go to the child who carried out the father's wishes.

IV Discussion:

The knowledge obtained by even this brief glimpse into the dynamics of these children who have killed may yield some practical benefit if it can be used to prevent such tragedies.

Diligent attention to the many distress signals sent up by these troubled families would have been the first and most essential step in the preventive chain, alerting the environment to the existence of a *lethal situation*. Only then could prompt, effective action be taken to head off catastrophe. Clinical programs providing crisis intervention for families with a *lethal situation* may have practical preventive value.

In the case of Freddie, many opportunities to intervene were presented to relatives, schools, and neighbors, for his plight and that of his unfortunate siblings were repeatedly brought to their attention. In the case of Gertrude, social agencies were informed by her mother that she thought her husband was psychotic and dangerous. She was told by them that her husband was "just mean." Even a casual investigation of her home (the unfit home from which her older sister had already been removed!) would have revealed the pressure and dangers to which Gertrude later succumbed.

V Fear of Strong Emotions:

People often show a remarkable reluctance to intervene in "private fights," even when such intervention can be life-saving. Notorious examples of this reluctance make the headlines with depressing frequency. One has the impression that such reluctance is not caused by misapplied tact, nor even by cowardice. Rather, it seems to be an unconsciously-employed defense against exposing one's self to the potentially overwhelming emotional impact of flagrant aggression and sadism.

Such overt displays of raw id create anxiety in observers by threatening to weaken their inner control over their own repressed impulses. Even "professionals" may avoid taking necessary and appropriate action in these situations. All too often our emotions also blind us to the possibilities such cases offer for study and treatment. Rather than use the opportunity they present to us, we are tempted to avoid them altogether, or to dispose of them as quickly as possible. The importance of these cases to the expansion of our knowledge of human behavior is such that they should be given much more attention and study.

VI Study of Children Who Kill:

In many states, the Juvenile Court system has the effect of removing the threat of criminal prosecution in cases of homicide perpetrated by children. (See the Juvenile Code of almost any state or the Federal Juvenile Delinquency Act.) This fact may permit serious study of the child who kills someone, without the impediment which the legal threat of self-incrimination would pose for the adult murderer. (It is recognized that guilt, shame, repression and other inner impediments to free communication would not be automatically removed by this exculpation.) This circumstance provides a *unique* opportunity to study what is usually hidden from view. It seems worthwhile, therefore, to propose that, through consultation with judges and lawyers to provide suitable legal safeguards, ground rules should be set up for the study of children who kill and the social and psychological setting involved in the killing. Such study may identify strategic points in the development of the *lethal situation* at which preventive intervention may be effective, as well as other facets of this shocking but seldom studied act.

VII Summary:

This paper has suggested that children who kill may have been recipients of both overt and covert "commands" to commit murder from their adult environment. Several modes of communication are identified, together with the peculiar family relationships within which these communications took place. Such events should alert the sophisticated observer to the danger of impending violence. Once alerted, the observer should become a rescuer and should extricate the child from the *lethal situation*. He should not allow himself to be dissuaded from action by the fear of the misdiagnosis or of causing a fuss, or by any of the usual rationalizations which bystanders employ to justify their failure to act.

REFERENCES

1. Ardrey, R.: *African Genesis,* New York: Atheneum, 1961.
2. Sargent, D. A.: Social Work 7:35, 1962.

AGGRESSION: ADAPTIVE AND DISRUPTIVE ASPECTS

Peter L. Giovacchini, M.D.

Since Freud's monograph "Beyond the Pleasure Principle"[1] aggression has become a controversial basic concept in metapsychology. The evaluation of a patient's aggressive reactions is clinically useful, but when one attempts to make judgments regarding a patient's ability to maintain psychic balance, there is considerable confusion. Furthermore, the distinctions between aggression, hostility, violence and rage are unclear.

Aggression, hostility, rage and other terms that have some relationship to activity and violence are at various conceptual levels. For example, rage can be considered an affect; aggression, an energic modality; hostility and violence are usually discussed phenemonologically, i.e., behaviorally.

Nevertheless, one can postulate important relationships among these various expressions if they are viewed in terms of emotional development.

These different conceptual frames of reference can be thought of as a hierarchal continuum. The neonate's purposeless, chaotic screaming and kicking represent the primitive end of the continuum which is primary-process oriented. Active, aggressive, non-hostile behavior, in the service of adaptation and mastery, represents the other end of the spectrum which is more mature and secondary-process oriented.

The intermediary stages range from such reactions and states as disruptive rage—uncontrollable anger and violence—to reactive and justifiable anger that leads to purposeful action. There are, of course, many gradations, but the main progression is from reactions that are essentially maladaptive to those which are goal-oriented.

This spectrum also can be considered from the viewpoint of the different

Dr. Giovacchini is a professor in the Department of Psychiatry, University of Illinois College of Medicine, Chicago. This paper originally appeared in amplified form in the *Bulletin of the Philadelphia Association for Psychoanalysis*, 19:76-86, 1969.

frames of references mentioned above, and, here again, one can postulate a hierarchal continuum. The neonate's "tantrum" is obviously an overwhelming motoric response to some inner state of homeostatic inbalance. What he feels under these circumstances is impossible to ascertain. But in view of his developmental immaturity it seems likely that he does not have sufficient psychic organization to have a structured emotional experience. An affect, even hate,[2] presupposes a degree of psychic structure that the neonate has not yet achieved. Consequently, his tantrum can be considered a massive, diffuse, motoric manifestation of a state of psychic disruption, one which antedates feelings of rage and frustration.

With further development, the child gains the capacity to "feel" in a more sophisticated, non-visceral fashion. From a sensory viewpoint, his experiencing of satisfaction or dissatisfaction is mentationally richer. Affects of pleasure and pain develop, which at these still early stages do not lead to purposeful behavior.

The continuum from neonatal tantrums to goal-directed, aggressive behavior is a description of various motor and sensory characteristics of different developmental stages. It should be emphasized that there are many other qualities that characterize these different stages, and that this conceptual scheme does not make any statements about etiological links. The achievement of reality-oriented aggression need not be a consequence of neonatal screaming. The development of the psychic apparatus is a complex phenomenon, dependent upon many variables.

What we are viewing here are essentially responses that are manifestations of various psychic states. In a sense, these responses may be considered end products; and, as such, one response does not lead directly to another one. Each structural level, however, leads to the next "higher" one, and the characteristic qualities of one level can be compared to those of another level. These comparisons are essential to clinical and therapeutic concepts of regression and progression. The following vignette illustrates these points.

The patient, a single man in his early 20's, presented a benign, cheerful exterior. He formed friendly relationships easily. They seldom lasted, however, and this transience was one of the reasons he sought therapy. During the early phases of treatment, it soon became apparent that insofar as his friendliness was overdone, his benign demeanor represented a defensive facade.

He used such primitive defenses as projection, but in a novel fashion. Unlike the typical paranoid, what he projected was friendly and helpful instead of hostile and persecutory. For example, if he were facing a difficult decision the "voices" would discuss the situation and eventually help him reach an agreeable decision.

After the adaptive (defensive) nature of his friendliness was interpreted, the patient changed dramatically. He became frightened. His behavior generally and in my office was infantile. His frustration tolerance diminished, and the most trivial and slightest stimuli caused him to feel intense anger. At first he whined, but after several weeks he became very angry, and eventually his anger reached the proportions of a tantrum. He would writhe and kick on the couch, scream and cry, clenching and unclenching his fists, beating his head and striking the wall. On one occasion, he rolled off the couch, thrashed around on the floor, and started biting a loose rug until I made him stop.

He again changed when I indicated that I could not tolerate the intensity of his tantrums. He continued being very angry, but in a more controlled fashion. He now resembled the traditional paranoid patient.

I was made into the chief persecutor. His benign voices had left him a long time ago, and now he heard the more usual persecutors generally threatening and accusing him of being a homosexual. He believed that I had hired these persecutors to torment him.

His paranoid system became well stabilized, but after considerable vacillation. From time to time he would feel less intense about me, at which juncture he would seek me as an ally in some cause against social injustices, and in inverse proportion to the paranoid transference. Finally, he became less involved with social issues and saw me as the exclusive persecutor. The therapeutic handling of this case is tangential to the thesis of this paper. He had a sufficiently well-established therapeutic alliance so that he was able to develop insights about the paranoid transference.

Although the course of regression and progression was not a steady one, there was some direction to the general movement. He gradually became affectively less paranoid as he was able to recognize the adaptive qualities of his behavior (to control an otherwise disruptive rage). His ego "progressed" from a psychotic organization to one in which he could view his surrounding world in a less delusional manner. This forward movement was characterized by the same preoccupation with social issues that he had prior to entering his phase of organized paranoia.

At the beginning of this phase he was fervently involved with these issues. My own prejudices and orientation caused me to feel these were laudatory causes and *therefore* realistic, but in spite of my implicit approval, I recognized that his involvement was exclusive of all other phases of his life.

Gradually, as he needed the involvement less, he did not feel as "immersed" in these activities and was able to handle himself in a more calm and objective fashion. He was less intense and less passive generally, becoming aggressive in many other areas.

Discussion

The description of this patient's regression and subsequent progression can bring into focus many important aspects of the effects of hostile responses upon the psychic economy. From a theoretical viewpoint, I would like to emphasize the following areas:

1. The general effects of hostile acting-out upon psychic integration; i.e., whether it is disruptive or adaptive and whether it leads to regression or structuralization.

2. The degree of organization of various hostile impulses and affects and the qualities of the corresponding ego states.
3. The significance of such impulses and affects relevant to developmental phases.

Adaptation and disruption are in themselves relative concepts. Even during a regressive course, the resultant ego state may be considered adaptive and defensive. Yet, it is a product of regression and insofar as it contains less organization, it is relatively maladaptive and can be thought of as a disruption of a higher state of psychic organization.

Reviewing the hierarchal continuum discussed earlier, screaming and tantrums do not seem to be associated with later states of higher organization. One cannot comment about the subjective state of the neonate. However if the mother isn't able to furnish gratification that will calm him, the child finally becomes utterly exhausted, a state which does not seem to have any advantages with reference to emotional development. He seems depleted.

When an adult reacts as an infant, one can make more definite statements about his psychic organization. My patient did not seem to gain from experiencing intense rage. It was a helpless, impotent rage that caused him to feel frightened and vulnerable.

When he started a tantrum early in a session, he was "spent" at the end. He often felt that he would be totally unable to face the world outside my office, and his self-confidence and self-esteem were very low. His reaction had the quality of a negative feedback. Infantile rage, whatever its source, became dominant.

This psychic state was one which threatened his adult ego-ideal. To behave in such a childish manner caused him considerable shame. Furthermore, it recapitulated an infantile ego state (one of relative disorganization) where he lacked the adaptive mechanisms to adjust to the demands of an adult world. Consequently, shame and feelings of inadequacy with accompanying helplessness caused him to experience additional anger.

His anger was not sufficiently organized to lead to outwardly-directed violence, but its self-destructive aspects were obvious, as demonstrated by his behavior in my office. As his shame increased, the destructive aspects of his superego became dominant, making the previously benign aspects inoperative.[3]

Obviously, this kind of psychic state cannot be endured indefinitely, and the patient had to construct defenses to protect himself from such an intolerable regression. At this point, his anger became more organized and focalized. This was a paranoid adjustment, but nevertheless an adjustment in which his ego integrity was partially restored. His paranoid projections, therefore, represented an adaptation. It was a delusional adaptation, but one which definitely represented a progression from the previous state. He could now cope with the surrounding world, and he eventually was able to restrict his persecutors to my office.

His paranoid adjustment was characterized by vigilance. He constantly scrutinized situations and events to assess whether they represented a threat. He looked at everything in terms of its potential for danger. He was chronically angry and he saw the world mainly in terms of violence. Still, this outlook achieved security because he could now put what had previously been uncontrollable disruptive anger outside of himself and then protect himself from it. Anger had now become a modality, an affect which was instrumental in maintaining ego integrity.

It is interesting to note how his persecutors, who, as mentioned above, were often projected onto me, changed and became "socialized." The patient's fervent involvent with civil liberty issues was also a defensive stabilization. In a sense, it was an *institutionalized paranoia*. He could fuse certain unacceptable parts of his self-image with some aspects of his environment and then react as if these unacceptable parts were outside of himself.

His defenses became socially acceptable. Consequently, his self-esteem was boosted and he began to function more effectively. Here we have an example of a positive feedback which had a psychopathological basis, but which, nonetheless, led to stability and created a setting where therapy could be effective.

In this instance, hostility, dependent upon its context, was both disruptive and adaptive. There was a continuum from primitive disruptive rage reactions to a somewhat reality-attuned anger, which led to aggressive and productive behavior. During regression the patient passed through the various phases of the continuum in the direction of infantile tantrums; and during progression, he reversed his direction, going through similar phases.

Many adolescent patients demonstrate similar mechanisms. Their involvement with social issues as an almost exclusive preoccupation, has a paranoid flavor to it and maintains an otherwise precarious equilibrium.

Hostility, therefore, can be studied in the context of emotional development. Now, I will review the three categories of anger—infantile tantrums, general paranoid reactions, and institutionalized paranoia—in terms of their corresponding ego states and the developmental scale.

My patient's chaotic rage reactions occurred when he was experiencing symbiotic fusion in the transference to the analyst, behavior which many therapists would consider psychotic. At these moments he did not distinguish himself from me and often called me by his name, as well as the reverse, referring to himself by my name. His dreams emphasized the dissolution of ego boundaries, depicted by such manifest content as drowning or being engulfed by both inanimate objects and me. These dreams and transference feelings were not in themselves threatening and frightening. After he began to believe that I could not fulfill his omnipotent expectations, he developed chaotic tantrums.

Direct observations of children sometimes illustrate similar factors. Bettelheim and Ekstein give many examples of the emotional upheavals of autistic children, which have been conceptualized by Mahler in terms of the symbiotic phase of development.[4, 5, 6]

The following situation illustrates the genesis of a tantrum within the context of the symbiotic phase. An 11-month old boy was being observed through a one-way mirror as he played, his mother sitting quietly in the background. He crawled on the floor and handled several different toys. At times, he was obviously frustrated but he never turned to his mother for help. He totally ignored her and ploddingly continued handling the various toys.

The mother unobtrusively left the room as planned. Although her son seemed to have ignored her presence and hardly noticed her departure, he broke down in a fierce tantrum. He screamed, thrashed and kicked, and banged his head on the floor. He was inconsolable when a staff member tried to calm him. Finally the mother came back into the room. His tantrum disappeared instantaneously and he continued playing as before, once again ignoring her presence.

The history of this boy's illness, as well as that of my adult patient, indicates that primitive rage occurred in the context of a symbiotic developmental phase. The child could maintain a defiant autonomy as long as the mother was around. He seemed to be using this behavior to control her but actually she was vital for his equilibrium within this symbiotic relationship. When she left, he lost self-control. Both the child and my patient demonstrate that the mother or analyst is necessary as an auxiliary or fused ego in order for patients in a symbiotic phase to maintain ego functioning. Withdrawal by the symbiotic partner, or the partner's inadequacy to fulfill the other's needs, leads to a disintegration manifested by a purposeless rage. The latter seemed also to be a reaction against the loss of a symbiotic fusion.

The paranoid defense also can be viewed in terms of symbiosis. This patient and others have had mothers who use their children as a narcissistic extension of their hated selves. For many reasons, they are threatened by structuralization in their children beyond the symbiotic fusion, i.e., by the child's individuation. The child reacts by perceiving further structuralization as dangerous. In the adult, the paranoid projection represents a defensive attempt against this danger.

My patient's initial symptoms are interesting when compared with his paranoid reactions in the transference. He had always used projective defenses, but at first their content was benign and only later did they become more traditionally paranoid in their attacking and persecutory qualities. Still, as emphasized, the latter state was highly organized when compared to the previous chaos.

In a well-established therapeutic relationship the paranoid material gradually becomes less grim. The patient not only begins to look at his reactions with curiosity, but even when discussing persecutors, he does so in a calm and sometimes amused fashion. My patient was able to recall the benign voices as he began seeing the absurdity of some of his paranoid beliefs. He was then able to attribute some good intentions to his persecutors and was finally able to give them the capacity to behave logically and wisely.

Studying paranoid projections carefully often reveals a benign and partially synthesized core to the patient's externalized anger. To preserve themselves from the mother's assaultiveness, such patients "fragment" and they project the *healthier* parts of their egos to the outer world. True, the projections usually contain hostile destructiveness and are experienced as persecutory, but this may represent a super-structure. The introjected mother's destructiveness is superimposed upon more structured ego fragments.

The fragmentizing process represents an attempt to maintain a degree of autonomy and individuation, as well as a striving for further development. Even though this is a psychotic reaction, it is still an attempt to maintain synthesis. Its direction is forward, a progression with the goal of further structuralization and ego development. This paranoid reaction is designed to prevent a submergence of the self into a symbiotic fusion where all elements of individuation are lost. Viewing the paranoid adjustment in terms of its positive and structuralizing qualities leads to therapeutic advantages.

Summary

Angry, violent reactions were conceptualized in terms of a hierarchal continuum, purposeless tantrums representing the primitive end of the spectrum and active, non-hostile, aggressive behavior in the service of mastery, the other end. The intermediary positions emphasized paranoid mechanisms leading to persecutory delusions, followed by angry involvement at a more socialized level with various causes. The latter was referred to as an institutionalized paranoia.

The adaptive and disruptive aspects of the above responses were discussed. In this context, the corresponding ego states were described and the clinical reactions of anger and violence were examined, both in terms of their structure and their economic position in the developmental continuum.

REFERENCES

1. Freud, S.: *Beyond the Pleasure Principle*, Stand Edit, Vol. 18, London, 1920.
2. Winnicott, D. W.: Int J Psychoanal, Vol. 30, 1949.
3. Schafer, R.: Psychoanal Stud Child, Vol. 15 Internat Univ Press, New York, 1960.
4. Bettelheim, B.: *The Empty Fortress*. Infantile Autism and the Birth of the Self, The Free Press, New York, 1968.
5. Ekstein, R.: *Children of Time and Space, and of Action and Impulse*, Appleton-Century-Crofts, New York, 1966.
6. Mahler, M.: Psychoanal Stud Child, Vol. 7, Internat Univ Press, New York, 1952.

PSYCHOTHERAPY OF A TERRIFIED COMMUNIST

Richard D. Chessick, M.D.

In October 1965, I began treating a 24-year-old white single male, who appeared in my office dressed in a dark raincoat, which he kept wrapped tightly around him throughout the sessions. He was of medium height and slenderly-built, with an asthenic, almost artistic face. The individual facial features were rather coarse; his light brown hair was cut in ordinary fashion and his brown eyes were rimmed by prominent framed glasses. He was able to give a fluent history with quite appropriate affect, except when the subject of politics came up.

Whenever any mention of the United States or of politics of any kind took place—and it often did because he was quite preoccupied with the subject—he rather quickly began shouting and would continue to sound as if he were haranguing a crowd. It was almost impossible to interrupt him and definitely impossible to contradict or argue with him.

His viewpoints were essentially out of the *Peking Review*. He regarded the United States' positions on all matters as identical to those of Nazi Germany; he fervently believed in the violent overthrow of the government of the United States and hoped it would be replaced by a government similar to that of Communist China. He hoped for atomic war resulting in a Communist Chinese takeover of the world, and believed the death of millions of people would be justified for this end.

His request for treatment had nothing to do with his political beliefs, which he regarded as correct and superior to those of the "sheep" in America. Amazingly, his chief complaint was shyness! He claimed that he could not talk to people in the sense of making "small talk"; either he maintained an embarrassing silence or he would launch into one of his communist tirades.

Dr. Chessick is associate Professor of Psychiatry at Northwestern University Medical School, Chicago, Illinois.

As might be anticipated, he felt extremely awkward in all social situations, and was repeatedly teased for always doing the gauche thing.

He lived in a small apartment with his parents and sister. The sister was three years younger, a teacher, doing apparently well, who married during the patient's first year of therapy and subsequently had a baby.

The home situation had become intolerable for him both because of his frustration with himself, and because of his mother's nagging and complaining about financial matters. He was left going to school at night and with nothing to do in the day but watch television, dodge his mother's lady friends out of embarrassment, and do push-ups to "prepare" himself for the draft if he were ever caught in it.

His plan had been to work full time in the day and go to college at night to avoid the draft. He had taken a job as a case worker at a local hospital. It was his first full time job. He found that he just could not get the instructions on the job straight; in a day or so the boss was irritated with him and spoke sharply to him. When that happened he became overwhelmed with anxiety and left the job and went home. He could simply not bring himself to seek another job.

When he had been 14 years old, he began psychotherapy once or twice a week with a social worker at Jewish Charities because of his many disturbing obsessive rituals. This therapy continued for about one and a half years. His grades improved in high school, but there was no significant change in his symptoms.

He received interpretations from the social worker involving his "oedipal problems," which he later reported without affect as follows: "I hate my father because I want to sleep with my mother. I kept him from sleeping with my mother by my nightmares." His main response to such interpretations was one of indifference. He did come in to therapy regularly and apparently formed some kind of positive relationship with the social worker.

Then the social worker changed agencies for reasons not clear and therapy was terminated. This was experienced by the patient as a crushing rejection and was a turning point in the boy's life.

The patient became convinced that "people are no damned good." He forced himself to stop his obsessive rituals. He avoided everyone except his few boy friends and a girl he occasionally dated. He began developing unusual political views. By the time he entered college he had a reputation in the family and in the neighborhood for the extreme political views as already described and for his awkwardness in all social situations.

His sexual life consisted of masturbation accompanied by phantasies of undressing attractive girls. He noted that he could not carry the phantasy farther than that, and he attributed this to lack of experience. There were no homosexual thoughts or experiences reported. He expressed strong interest in dating girls and getting married but felt extremely frustrated because he was so shy, and, of course, without a job he could never hope to marry.

The patient presented a complex diagnostic problem. He manifested schizoid, narcissistic, obsessive-compulsive, paranoid and depressive features. On the basis of this variegated symptomatology he perhaps would have to be classified as "borderline schizophrenic"[1, 2], or a "borderline patient"[3].

I believed that the psychodynamics of his case centered around abandonment and rejection. Considering the lack of adult figures for him to identify with in any healthy fashion and the desperate insecurity of his early years, it seemed remarkable that he developed as many defenses as he did, and used them as needed. I liked him in spite of all his protest and his extreme views, and in therapy with him I did a lot of listening without rejecting, especially for many months at the beginning. I indicated my disagreement with his views, but refused to argue with him about them.

At the core of the personality of this patient there clearly existed a deep yearning and striving for maternal gratification, and a profound fear of rejection and abandonment. He experienced this fear as a severe threat to his masculinity. Passivity, homosexuality, annihilation and castration were all confused in his mind, and required a vigilant set of ego defenses.

Among this set of defenses, the ego operations of most theoretical interest here were those leading to the development of his political views. Some of his views, especially those about the motivations of our President and members of his cabinet, sounded like delusions to me—but in China they would have been routine.

Perhaps these political views could be be called a compromise between having a full blown paranoid delusional system and keeping in touch with reality. He chose an intellectual structure for his thinking that still permitted him to maintain a contact with the real world, and that at the same time provided a vehicle of discharge for his rage. It also protected him against his longings to become close to anybody, as in the classical paranoid equation described by Freud.

We might call this an intermediate stage in the development of a paranoid system, and it is of great theoretical interest. The second consideration of theoretical interest lies in exploring the relationship of such intermediate stages in the forming of delusional systems to intermediate stages in the development of overt aggressive behavior. A case with some similarities to this one was described by Lindner[4]. He writes:

Within the Party, Mac could give vent to his hatred and aggression—originally directed against Ma and later the world—with almost unlimited freedom. It not only permitted him to express these qualities, but directed them upon a broad segment of society, channelized them toward a plentitude of objects, gave him the words and even the techniques to implement them.

At the same time, although the communist system permitted Mac's indulgence in aggression, it also required a certain discipline or control so there need be no fear that it would get out of hand.

My patient did not join the party, but controlled matters by restricting the aggression to vocal statements without accompanying overt behavior. So, just as with Lindner's patient, the communist system protected the patient from paranoid breakdown—the next step in dealing with such overwhelming rage—or from overt aggression with all the disastrous consequences of being, as Lindner put it, ". . . treated like a mad dog and destroyed for it."

Lindner also recognized the deep dependent longing for security underneath the aggression, and the attempt to use a system that had clear answers for everything as "something to latch on to".

In any discussion of violence and aggression we must distinguish between what Robert Penn Warren calls "status homicide" and "homicide for gain" on the one hand, and "anonymous homicide" on the other[5]. "Homicide for gain" and "status homicide," in which murder is based on an intensely personal thwarting of some kind, are traditional forms of homicide in our world, but, as Warren writes:

> The kind we have now is really new. Killing an old man on a park bench, reading his papers, smoking his morning cigar. He's dead suddenly because some kid decided to kill him. This is another kind of homicide. There's a whole new world of violence, violence of a kind not in the sociological categories 30 years ago.

Perhaps the most dramatic portrayal of "anonymous homicide" is found in Albee's play, *The Zoo Story*. Compare this, for example, to the intensely personal violence of the traditional kind in Dreiser's *An American Tragedy*.

A third fascinating, vital and timely question raised is why my patient chose an autoplastic instead of an alloplastic solution to his difficulties. We see him attempting to deal with his terrific aggression—regardless of its source—in obsessional, depressive and paranoid ways. But he develops a severe reaction formation to overt aggression.

I don't believe anyone has the answer to this question. If we could understand the ego systems involved in this choice much better, perhaps we would have an important preventive tool to offer in curbing the development of "anonymous homicide."

Some new efforts in this direction have been made in a recent book by Storr[6]. He points out the universal nature of paranoid tendencies and the proclivity to brutality in all people, which he views as rooted in the biological nature of man. The intense frustrations of an unsatisfactory childhood give rise to overwhelming aggressions, which can be channeled either into paranoid delusions without aggression, direct sadistic behavior, or a combination of both.

The development of extreme political views, whether on the right wing or the left wing, can be understood in some cases as an intermediate formation by the ego in order to prevent the development of either full-blown paranoid psychosis, or anonymous murderous behavior, or both. It then becomes clear why all such fanatical views have so much in common and are so predicated on continuing violence and senseless destruction.

An interesting question immediately comes to mind, implied by Barry Goldwater's controversial statement, "Extremism in defense of liberty is no vice." Although it is obvious that some political conditions can be so unbearable as to justify extreme and revolutionary solutions, this matter is actually more a philosophical than a clinical question.

In my clinical experience, both at the Federal Prison in Lexington, Ky. and in private practice, it never has been difficult to identify patients who use these extremist positions as ego defensive operations. The quasi-delusional quality of the beliefs, the inaccessibility to debate, the over-simplification of issues and the pre-occupation with violence and destruction, in an individual with a paucity of deep human relations, are typical features of these patients. In my opinion a significant proportion of extremists of all kinds in our country today fall into this category.

In summary, a borderline patient is presented who has embraced whole-heartedly the Maoist-Communist political ideology as the last step to ward off a full fledged paranoid delusional system, after obsessive and depressive defenses have failed. A discussion of the role of extremist political ideology as a defense against either full-fledged paranoia or uncontrolled anonymous homicide is presented.

Another important aspect of this case is found in the reaction-formation to aggression that construed the presenting complaint—"shyness." The question is raised but unanswered: why in this case did ego systems develop to protect the patient against violent aggressive acting out and subsequent destruction, whereas in other cases the solution is precisely such an "anonymous" aggression and senseless destruction?

REFERENCES

1. Knight, R. P.: *Psychoanalytic Psychiatry and Psychology,* edited by R. P. Knight. New York, Internat. Univ. Press, 1954.
2. Knight, R. P.: *Psychoanalytic Psychiatry and Psychology,* edited by R. P. Knight, New York, Internat. Univ. Press, 1954.
3. Chessick, R. D.: Amer J Psychother 22:655, 1968.
4. Lindner, R.: *The Fifty Minute Hour.* New York, Bantam Books, 1955.
5. Warren, R. P., et al: Symposium: Violence in Literature, American Scholar, 1968.
6. Storr, A.: *Human Aggression,* New York: Atheneum, 1968.

ON THE EGO RESTRAINT
OF VIOLENCE

Hyman L. Muslin, M.D. and
William J. Pieper, M.D.

The inhibition of aggression, as of any act, is multi-determined.[1] Thus, an aggressive act is ordinarily shaped and discharged with respect to the individual conscience and ego-ideal structures as well as in respect to the needs of the environment and the ego's defensive needs. It represents the instinctual derivative, modified and neutralized by a variety of specialized ego functions.

The important ego functions in either the restraint or discharge of aggressive and sexual drives, such as repression, neutralization and synthesis, are of major significance in the final aggressive action, because the integrity of these functions determines the shape, form and intensity of the act. Other ego apparatuses, such as reality-testing and perception, are of the essence in the initiation of aggressive activity. This can readily be observed in the major anxiety and hostility seen in schizophrenics who perceive their environment as malevolent.

The superego functions serve a major role in either the discharge or restraint of a particular instinctual derivative. Depending on the nature of the instinctual drive and the concepts of the superego, the superego may facilitate drive discharge; it may serve to stimulate ego defenses against the particular drive; or, as a censor, it may stimulate feelings of wrongdoing.

We present the hypothesis that in states of marked (traumatic state) anxiety such as those that precede violence, the ego functions, including the self-observing function, are severely and selectively impaired, so that instinctual derivatives are discharged without the filters or restraints noted above. Thus a state of suspension of the psychological being—a state of "psychic decortication"—is present. A human operating without benefit of ego function is seen.

Dr. Muslin is professor of psychiatry and director of the Medical Student Training Program in Psychiatry at the University of Illinois College of Medicine, Chicago, where Dr. Pieper is clinical assistant professor of psychiatry.

Hartmann has discussed the failure in the ego's neutralizing function, such as that seen in schizophrenia, as a major ego defect in these conditions.[2] In an acute outburst of violence, manifestations of a more widespread process of dehumanization may be observed in which there is more or less total cessation of regulation of drive discharge. The following case history represents a summary of many diagnostic interviews between one of the authors (WJP) and a patient who had recently committed a violent homicidal act, killing his girl friend without apparent cause.

The patient was a single male in his mid-20's from whom the following data were obtained after he had been incarcerated for the murder of his fiancée. The patient came from an intact, middle-class home and was an only child. His father was a white-collar worker at the lower end of the middle-management scale. His mother did not work. The family lived in a modest dwelling which they owned in a stable urban community. He went to the local neighborhood primary grade school and the community high school where he was a superior student. As far as can be determined from history his social adaptation in school was considered above average. He dated, was an accomplished musician and had several friends.

While in college he became engaged to marry a girl he had known for several years and who was a fellow student in the same school. Their relationship was characterized by intensely intimate feelings combined with suspicious, even jealous, attitudes on the girl's part, and a fluctuating wish to terminate the engagement on the patient's part.

For a year or so prior to the murder their relationship had been characterized by frequent arguments and temporary break-ups followed by reunions. It was during this time that the patient sought counseling in the student health service of his school with the presenting complaints of moodiness and depression.

Three months before the murder the patient's mother contracted a blood dyscrasia that often is fatal. This illness necessitated her hospitalization. To our knowledge, this was the first instance of a life-threatening disease in the home. Up to that point both parents had been well. The mother's disease was controlled medically to the point of a clinical remission and three days before the murder she returned home to convalesce.

One day before the murder the counseling which the young man had been receiving in the student health service was terminated by mutual agreement. As he recalled, the day of the murder began and progressed uneventfully. School was not in session at the time and he was at home. His father had gone to work as usual, and his mother was seemingly doing well and was up and about in the home.

The patient and his fiancée had decided to go for a casual automobile drive. They had not been quarreling that day, though his fiancée had become more demanding of his time and suspicious of him of late.

As he then described the homicide, they were parked in an isolated spot when he suddenly reached for a screwdriver and began stabbing her repeatedly. His recall of this event seemed quite accurate regarding the actions, for he could remember the look on her face as he was stabbing the life out of her body. At some point during his frenzied attack he thought of Othello and Desdemona. When he was through and she was in an apparently agonal state, he attempted to get help for her but to no avail.

During the interview the patient evinced intense emotions of grief, atonement and sorrow for what he had done, but despite much self-probing he could not understand his motive for the act. To him the entire tragedy was an experience executed through him by a *deus ex machina;* i.e., the entire event as it occurred was totally foreign to him despite his detailed recall of the actual event.

He claimed no premeditation whatsoever and could not specify a triggering event prior to the moment when he "found" himself, so to speak, murdering his fiancée. Autopsy disclosed that the girl was *not* pregnant; the patient disclaimed any fears along this line.

To summarize, in regard to the murderer's experience of the murder act: he could recall the event in detail but without being able to recall the affect, if any, he had experienced during the event. He never did understand why he killed his fiancée but when discussing it in retrospect he evinced intense emotions of grief, atonement and sorrow.

Additional data from extensive psychological testing revealed no significant findings about the subject's homicidal potentials; the data from the examinations were typical for the clinical diagnosis of a mixed hysterical and compulsive-obsessive neurosis; there was no evidence of a thinking disorder. The patient's physical and laboratory examinations were normal, including a normal EEG.

Discussion

As noted previously, the ego's ability to function in diverse ways to restrain instinctual derivatives is a reflection of the tension in the psychic apparatus. As Kris has pointed out, the higher ego functions are crippled by severe degrees of anxiety.[3]

On another level, the apparatuses available for restraint, especially restraint of aggression, in animals other than human, operate in an instinctual fashion, as pointed out by Lorenz, Kaufman and others. These instinctive inhibitors are partly physiological, such as the mechanism protecting an animal from eating itself to death, and also partly based on certain percepts which are responded to with species-specific inhibitions. These percepts in most animals prevent infanticide and intraspecies killing. Blunting of these percepts therefore prevents these inhibitions from operating.

There is no analagous mechanism in humans. Intraspecies killings are prohibited only by percepts (i.e., internalized codes), a situation ubiquitously fraught with difficulty. Thus, without the ego apparatuses' integrated functioning to serve as restraint, there are no other mechanisms to inhibit instinctual urges.

The ego functions which are intrinsic to the restraint of violence constitute a variety of operations that modify and stunt the destructive drive. At the point of the violent act, such as in the case material we have described, the patient experienced an absence of those functions necessary to restrain the primitive aggressive drive. Further, there was an absence of modifying, harmonizing functions which would enable a discharge of aggression adaptive to the environment, as well as in harmony with regard to other psychic structures (superego, etc.).

Also noted in the patient's description of the tragic event was the absence of the capacity for self-observation, observing himself as an object interacting with another object. As the patient described the happening, he clearly perceived the female and himself but was not able to assign human properties to either himself or the "object" of his attack.

Thus, the cognitive function of perception was present in a skeletal sense. However, the capacity for perception was severely limited at that moment and the young man could perceive neither himself as object, nor environmental objects, beyond reporting what he was doing and how the face of his fiancée appeared to him. He was not capable of introspection so as to perceive another object suffering.

Beyond the perceptual defects, the patient, from his report, apparently was incapable of registering (i.e., experiencing) any mental state of pleasure or non-pleasure. This fact can also be understood as a manifestation of a defect in the perception of the self. The patient was at that point not only experiencing a momentary regression (objectless, both internally and environmentally), but he was in a state of non-being. He had an absence of experience.

This point of view emphasizes only the importance of the ego structure involved in this event. Viewing the action as a destructive attack against a transference object (part object, etc.) is not germane because the patient was in a state of objectlessness (i.e., was without useable memory traces of himself or of any other object). This specific ego defect in perception also helps to explain why super-ego signals were not functional; there was no perception of these signals.

To return to our original formulation, the notion was advanced that in some cases of anxiety, ego functions are interrupted in their operation, and a variety of effects are seen. Thus, in the schizophrenic syndromes, massive anxiety ushers in gross regression (i.e., aggressivization, libidinization) of many ego functions over a period of time. The stimulus for the anxiety (and therefore regression) is spread over a long period, and the regressive process ushered in also takes place over a long period.

In the case we have presented, a very brief period was involved in the initiation of the anxiety and, as seen, the entire attack was brief, terminating with a return of ego interests and superego function. The cathexis necessary for optimal performance of various ego functions is that of a charge of neutralized energy.[4] In the wake of severe intrapsychic conflict with unbound anxiety, such cathexis is not present, and defects in ego functioning are manifest.

Summary

We have presented a case of violence focusing on aspects of, and deficits in, ego functioning. Diagnostically, the case material reflects features of a traumatic state with a dissociative reaction. Further investigation possibly would reveal aspects of the transference-meaning of the behavior, as well as other data from the genetic point of view and data from the dynamic and other metapsychological viewpoints.

Our intent, however, was to describe the ego considerations of violence to which this case material lent itself. These considerations, of course, cannot be generalized because each case of violence and each psychic apparatus involved must be investigated separately.

What seems to us to be a generic consideration is that in those cases of violence stemming from intrapsychic conflict and failures to resolve conflict, those ego functions which represent a human approach to life are deemed ineffective. This consideration seems to us to make the best case for a preventive psychiatry aimed at establishment and re-establishment of ego mechanisms to maintain repressions and to facilitate adaptation to the environment.

REFERENCES

1. Waelder, R.: Psychoanal Quart 5:45, 1936.
2. Hartmann, H.: Psychoanal Stud Child 8:177, 1953.
3. Kris, E.: Int J Psychoanal 17:285, 1936.
4. Hartman, H.: J Amer Psychoanal Ass Monogr Series, No. 1, N. Y. International Univ. Press, 1958.

SECTION III

RESEARCH INVESTIGATIONS

Many of the papers appearing in the previous two sections can properly be considered research at various levels. This section was set apart because the papers grouped under this heading present more basic and specific investigations of aggression and violence than those found earlier in the book.

As in previous sections, the diverse topics covered here illustrate the range of perspectives from which aggression and violence must be considered. Some readers may be surprised by Dr. Leonard Berkowitz's conclusions, based on investigations of the effect of expression of hostile feelings on aggressive behavior. His findings raise again interesting questions concerning the possible influence of mass media on violent behavior.

Dr. David Rothstein's thoughtful comments on the study of assassination victims and Dr. Augustus Kinzel's investigations of factors promoting physical violence among prison inmates represent knowledge gained through examination of very specific aspects of violent behavior.

Possible biogenetic roots of violence are probed in Dr. Benson Ginsburg's report of experiments aimed at uncovering complex interactions between genetic and biochemical factors and experiential variables at critical periods. These experiments suggest some awesome possibilities for future control of violent behavior.

Studies of mechanisms for coping with aggressive feelings provide an important approach to the control and redirection of violent impulses in both individuals and groups. Certainly, further studies of factors which enable both individuals and groups to cope with aggressive drives and to channel them in directions other than violent behavior should provide better techniques of successful conflict resolution and modification of violent behavior. Dr. Daniel Offer's paper describing means by which normal adolescents cope with aggressive feelings is an example of this approach. Further analyses and definitions of what constitutes violent behavior in adolescents by Drs. Rolde and Goethals add to our understanding of the adaptive aspects of certain forms of behavior in adolescents.

These papers illustrate the wide range of significant variables in an approach to violent behavior, as well as the valuable, sometimes surprising, findings that can develop from carefully planned research efforts. It is hoped that these examples will illustrate the potential value of such efforts and encourage more research into the understanding and control of human violence.

Violent behavior may be one of the most difficult phenomena to investigate. The sporadic, unplanned occurrence of violent behavior as well as the anxiety it produces in observers because of the fantasied, sometimes real, possibility of being its target, and the difficulty of maintaining neutral positions in often polarized violent situations, all tend to limit the possibilities for investigation.

Among the problems not touched on by papers in this section are the barriers encountered in the communication and application of research findings to "real" situations. Obviously much more research, knowledge, and effective communication with those individuals who are in a position to use this information in various contexts are urgently needed.

EXPERIMENTAL INVESTIGATION OF HOSTILITY CATHARSIS

Leonard Berkowitz, Ph.D.

Several years ago the movie "The Tenth Victim" proposed a straightforward and dramatic method for controlling violence and limiting wars: the most aggressive people in society should try to kill each other in a socially sanctioned hunt, with the winner gaining a fortune. The hunters would drain their pent-up aggressive urges by killing or trying to kill others—or by dying. Onlookers, participating vicariously in the hunt, would also discharge their hostile energy as they watched the goings-on. With all of this drainage of energy taking place in the hunt, there would be no aggression left for extracurricular violence or for wars.

Essentially similar proposals based on theoretically comparable analyses have been advanced by other writers. Lorenz tells us that members of socially isolated groups must inevitably experience a build-up of aggressive drive; outsiders aren't available to be attacked and thus provide an outlet for the accumulating aggressive energy.[1] The wise person in these circumstances, Lorenz says, would smash a vase with as loud and resounding a crash as possible. We don't have to destroy other people to reduce our aggressive urges; it's enough merely to destroy inanimate objects.

Of course, it may be expensive to go around breaking vases, and some people have argued for a much cheaper solution to the problem of violence: All that need be done is to show lots of aggression on the TV and movie screens. If this violates our aesthetic sensibilities, or if we grow tired of westerns and war movies, there is always competitive sports, or maybe canal-digging. And what about the race to the moon? Cannot these competitive and hazardous activities provide a "moral equivalent to war"—socially ac-

Dr. Berkowitz is Vilas Research Professor in Psychology at the University of Wisconsin, Madison.

ceptable and even constructive ways of reducing the aggressive drive?

The widespread popularity of these ideas is easily understood. They follow quite logically from *energy models* of motivation and especially from interpreting aggression as deriving from a special aggressive energy. These energy concepts probably are accepted more because of their readily understood metaphorical nature than because of their essential validity.

Although those who confine their reading to the traditional psychoanalytic literature[2, 3] and to the popular writings of Lorenz might not know this, energy analyses of motivation are falling into increasing disrepute among experimental biologists and psychologists. These analyses are much too simple and even hinder the search for important determinants of behavior.

In the case of aggression, the energy model usually maintains that a wide variety of activities (including fantasy, competitive sports, and indirect as well as verbal and physical aggression), in addition to involving many different types of individuals, can lower the person's inclination to attack others. However, a rapidly growing body of carefully controlled research raises serious questions about this overly simplified formulation, and even casts considerable doubt on its validity. Rather than producing a lowered probability of further violence, aggression in the absence of guilt or anxiety is all too likely to stimulate still more aggression.

If policymakers were to follow the classic concept of catharsis or accept the similar ideas of Lorenz as a guide for social action, the results could well be unfortunate indeed.

Alternatives to the energy model of aggression are provided by explanations based on ideas of stimulus-response relationships and learning. These alternative concepts are far better able to account for the available evidence concerning the expression of aggressive energy.

A decade of laboratory research has virtually demolished the contention that persons can resolve their aggressive tendencies by watching people beat each other up. Experiments with young children, high school and college students, and even older adults, have shown again and again that, under certain circumstances, witnessed aggression can *increase* the chances that the *observer* will behave more aggressively.

Several different processes seem to contribute to this increased probability of aggression. The observer learns something; he can acquire new aggressive action patterns imitatively through seeing how the aggressor behaves on the screen. Film violence may lower restraints against aggression in audience members, either by showing that aggression pays off or by seeming to legitimatize violence.

Several experiments conducted in my own laboratory illustrate this legitimatizing phenomenon. Deliberately provoked college students saw a filmed prize fight in which the protagonist, Kirk Douglas, received a bad beating. In some cases, the introduction to the film led the audience to regard the beating as "bad" and ethically unjustified; Kirk Douglas was said to be a "good guy."

By contrast, for other subjects, Kirk Douglas was portrayed in a much less sympathetic manner so that his beating was viewed as proper and justified. Later, when all of the students were given an opportunity to administer electric shocks to a person who had angered them, the subjects who were shown the latter (justified) film violence generally exhibited the stronger aggression.

It is as if the justified aggression on the screen made their own aggression seem morally proper, thereby temporarily lessening their inhibitions against aggression. (There is also the other side of the coin. Film violence that is regarded as "bad," unjustified or horrible serves to restrain the observers' later aggression.)

The "legitimate" movie violence did not lead to a fantasy catharsis. There was no purge of anger or discharge of hostile impulses through watching the screen villain getting the beating he deserved. Another experiment adds further corroboration to this point. All of the subjects were angered by the experimenter's confederate, and again, all saw the fight scene. This time, however, before the movie went on, one-third of the subjects were asked to imagine themselves as one of the film characters, the person who would beat up Kirk Douglas; another group was instructed to take the role of a watching judge; and a control group did no role-taking. The persons told to imagine themselves as the fight winner subsequently made stronger attacks via the administration of electric shocks on the experimenter's accomplice than did the members of either of the other groups. Make-believe as the winning aggressor led to more, not less, open aggression following the film.

At least one other process may be at work in witnessed violence, in addition to imitative learning and the lowering of restraints: The aggressive movie can stimulate transient aggressive ideas and *feelings* and even overt aggressive responses. There is nothing mysterious about this principle. It can be regarded as a special case of a much more general stimulus-response relationship. Simply put, stimuli that have frequently been associated with a certain type of action are capable of evoking that response on later occasions. If a certain stimulus has been repeatedly connected with aggressive behavior, it will be able to elicit aggressive responses from persons who are ready to act aggressively.

One such stimulus is a weapon, and several experiments have demonstrated that the mere presence of guns can heighten aggressive behavior. In at least two studies involving children playing with toy weapons, the aggressive gun-play led to an increase in aggressive encounters, such as fights with other youngsters.[4, 5] Many of these encounters were much more aggressive than just a continuation of make-believe shooting at each other. Here too, then, fantasy aggression did not increase peacefulness.

An experiment with college men also shows how weapons can stimulate aggressive reactions merely by being present.[6] Although non-angered subjects were not affected to any detectable extent, insulted men gave more electric shocks to their tormentor if weapons were visible than if neutral objects or no other objects were present with the shock machine. The weapons had evidently served as aggressive stimuli, eliciting stronger attacks from those subjects who, because they were angry, were ready to act aggressively.

Aggressive behavior, even aggressive words, also can furnish aggression-evoking stimuli. The sight of persons fighting, and perhaps especially seeing someone receive deserved or proper injury, certainly can provide these stimuli. *Geen* recently found that men who heard a loud but not painful sound after seeing a prize fight shocked their partners more readily than did other subjects who had not watched the fight or who had not heard the sound.[7] The excitation resulting from the loud sound had strengthened the aggressive reactions stimulated by the aggressive movie.

Sometimes the aggressive stimuli can come from our own behavior. We are often told that persons should verbally express their aggressive ideas and feelings. Telling someone we hate him supposedly will purge pent-up hostile inclinations and will "clear the air"—whatever this last cliche means. Maybe individuals can benefit sometimes and in some ways by candidly expressing feelings, but it is doubtful whether the use of hostile words will, in itself, lessen the likelihood of future aggression.

According to an experiment carried out at the State University of Iowa, college students required to speak aggressive words aloud in a learning task subsequently administered stronger electric shocks to a peer whenever he made a mistake than did a control group of subjects who had spoken only nonaggressive words.[8] There seems to have been a self-stimulation process here. The aggressive words apparently had stimulated aggressive responses which then strengthened the electric attacks on the other person.

It can, of course, be argued that the traditional concept of catharsis surely would not have gained such wide popularity if it did not have some basis in reality. Why do so many persons enjoy watching aggressive events or say that they feel better after seeing an aggressive game or movie? And further, how does one account for the pleasure that persons often feel after telling off or hurting someone?

I will try to show that there are several different mechanisms at work rather than a single energy discharge.

There is little doubt that many find pleasure in watching others fight. What is doubtful is that this pleasure necessarily signifies a reduction in the aggressive drive. Sometimes the pleasure stems from the ebb and flow of excitement; the game or match is simply an exciting event which is pleasant through the build-up and decline of internal tension. Angry persons, or those with a history of aggressive behavior, apparently are particularly inclined to seek out such aggressive scenes, according to at least one study.[9] But again, this seems to be due to the reinforcing quality of such scenes for them rather than to a discharge of aggressive energy.

Suggesting this, Hartmann found that deliberately-provoked juvenile delinquents exhibited a greater volume of aggression toward a peer (in the form of electric shocks) after watching a movie showing a boy receiving a painful beating in a fight, than after seeing a film focusing on the aggressor's actions.[10] The sight of the movie victim's suffering was presumably gratifying in some way—but enhanced their subsequent attacks on their own tormentor. 'Another reason why people say that they feel better after watching aggressive events is that they were so interested in the scene before them that they forgot their troubles, at least momentarily, and stopped brooding or stirring themselves up.

I have suggested here, on the basis of several different experiments, that the sight of someone being hurt is a reinforcement of aggression for angry people. As a reinforcement, this perception can lead to increased aggression, but may also produce a pleasant tension reduction, especially if the injured person represents a source of frustration.

A series of experiments by Hokanson and his students provides pertinent physiological evidence.[11] The college students in these investigations displayed a marked increase in systolic blood pressure after being insulted by the experimenter, and then showed a quick reduction in systolic pressure after they had an opportunity to give their tormentor electric shocks. There was a much slower decline in physiological tension (i.e., in systolic pressure), the researchers found, when the angered subject attacked someone other than his tormentor; displacing hostility was no more effective than no aggression at all in reducing physiological tension, according to this research.

The Hokanson studies also demonstrated that physical activity, in and of itself, does not lead to the rapid decline in systolic pressure, even when the motor responses are the same as those involved in the attacks on the tormentor. The subjects had to believe that they had attacked—and presumably hurt—their tormentor if the rapid decline in systolic pressure was to occur.

More recent experiments in this program suggest the cause of the decline in vascular response. Rather than being indicative of an energy discharge, reduction of physiological tension stems from prior rewarding experiences. That is, the rapid drop in blood pressure following aggression comes about to the extent that the person had previously learned that injuring his tormentor is rewarding or gratifying. Thus, when one group of subjects was rewarded for reacting nonaggressively to attacks made upon them, they later displayed the "cathartic"-like, quick decrease in vascular response only after behaving in a friendly, rather than a hostile, fashion.

Whatever the explanation, we evidently feel better when we see that the person who had angered us has been hurt. (Of course, the extent of the injury probably must be in keeping with our level of anger toward that person and our judgment of what he deserves.) We do not have to hurt the tormentor ourselves to experience this pleasure. In one of our Wisconsin studies, for example, angered subjects reported feeling better after hearing that their tormentor had performed poorly on an assigned task.

Similarly, in another study, deliberately provoked college students were more interested in listening to a tape recording in which their tormentor said he was suffering than in hearing him say that he was happy—even though the subjects were told that the tape recording had been made six to nine months earlier. In comparison to a nonangered group, the recording of the tormentor's earlier suffering also led to a greater expressed liking for that person than did a control recording in which the obnoxious person said he was in a neutral mood. If we are angry with someone, the knowledge that he has been hurt or has suffered is evidently gratifying.

This information is a reinforcement of aggression and, as such, can influence the probability of further aggression. We may stop or refrain from attacking our tormentor when we learn that he has been injured sufficiently, and we may feel much better than before. Retribution has been achieved. But this could well be only a temporary effect. Our habit of aggressiveness also has been reinforced so that, consequently, over the long run there actually is a greater likelihood that we will attack someone again in the future. There is empirical as well as theoretical support for this possibility. One research team observed the encounters among nursery school children over a nine-month period, taking particular note of aggressive and assertive actions. According to their data, the frequency of aggression by any one child *after* he had fought with another youngster was influenced by the victim's reactions to the initial attack. If the victim had reinforced the aggressor's behavior by showing defeat and submission, and perhaps some injury as well, there was an increased chance that the aggressor would again attack someone, particularly the first victim, later on.

The traditional energy model of aggression is clearly inadequate to account for many of the findings reported here. Not only is this conventional analysis much too simple, but it has also impeded recognition of the important roles played by environmental stimuli and learning in aggressive behavior. Above all, the energy model and the associated catharsis theory have helped to justify the expression of aggression, and have delayed our recognition of an important social principle: Aggression is all too likely to lead to still more aggression.

REFERENCES

1. Lorenz, Konrad: *On Aggression.* New York: Harcourt, Brace and World, 1966.
2. Hartmann, H., Kris, E., and Loewenstein, R., *Psychoanalytic Study of the Child,* Vols. 3-4, 1949.
3. Storr, Anthony: *Human Aggression.* New York: Atheneum, 1968.
4. Feshbach, S., *Journal of Personality,* Vol. 24, p. 449, 1956.
5. McCandless, D., *Journal of Personality and Social Psychology,* Vol. 4, p. 591, 1966.
6. Berkowitz, L., and Le Page, A., *Journal of Personality and Social Psychology,* Vol. 7, p. 202, 1967.
7. Geen, R., and O'Neal, E., *Journal of Personality and Social Psychology,* Vol. 11, p. 289, 1969.
8. Loew, C., *Journal of Personality and Social Psychology,* Vol. 5, p. 335, 1967.
9. Eron, I., *Journal of Abnormal and Social Psychology,* Vol. 67, p. 193, 1963.
10. Hartmann, D., *Journal of Personality and Social Psychology,* Vol. 11, p. 280, 1969.
11. Hokanson, J., and Edelman, R., *Journal of Personality and Social Psychology,* Vol. 3, p. 442, 1966.

THE ASSASSIN AND THE ASSASSINATED – as non-patient subjects of psychiatric investigation

David A. Rothstein, M.D.

Today, mankind is faced with two rather incongruous concerns. On the one hand, advances in the exploration of space confront us with the possibility of contaminating other planets with terrestrial life, which might adversely affect conditions on those planets, and would at least interfere with later scientific study of the origins of life.

On the other hand, we face the possibility of exterminating terrestrial life as we know it, because advances in technology have outrun advances in understanding how to handle constructively our own human aggressive impulses.

It is not just that we have not caught up with the nuclear technology of 1945, we have not even caught up with the far older technology of gunpowder and firearms.

It is my intention to discuss a certain approach to the problem of violence which has grown out of my experience in studying the assassination of President Kennedy.[1, 2, 3, 4] It is not an approach, however, which has to be limited to the issue of assassination. It is my essential aim in this paper to contend that the psychiatric study of individuals offers a potential for extrapolation to areas of larger scale public concern.

In a recent paper on Woodrow Wilson, Weinstein commented on the issue of understanding ". . . the way 'private' disturbances of behavior may be manifested in the world of public affairs."[5] I would enlarge this to a broader question of understanding how private *determinants* of behavior are manifested in the world of public affairs. In other words, I wish to *focus on such determinants* of behavior in a neutral way, rather than to label them as pathological or to categorize them as disturbances.

Dr. Rothstein is associate attending psychiatrist at the Psychosomatic and Psychiatric Institute, Michael Reese Hospital, Chicago, Illinois, and has served as consultant to the President's Commission on the Assassination of President Kennedy (Warren Commission) and the National Commission on the Causes and Prevention of Violence (Eisenhower Commission).

While continuing to work on the subject of Presidential assassination[6, 7] my interest began to broaden to include questions about the assassination victim. It has been contended by some writers that the victims of aggression, violence and even accidents have often unconsciously played a part in eliciting that violence.[8, 9, 10, 11] The awareness of this led me to wonder about whether there may be unconscious factors in the psychology of those who become Presidents or great leaders which might make them more prone to assassination, and whether any such factors might be more pronounced in some Presidents or leaders than in others.

We might expect some resistance to such an idea in the beginning, but if we could indeed work in the direction of discovering such factors, this might be of as much assistance in lowering the probability of assassination as would the understanding of the assassin.* For this reason I began to direct my attention toward available published data about Presidents and certain other great leaders (notably Charles DeGaulle, because he has *escaped* actual assassination attempts, and Dag Hammarskjold and Winston Churchill because of certain other qualities).

This led me to wonder even more generally about the personalities, about the psychological make-up of Presidents and other leaders, and I began to view my study of the threateners and of Oswald as only one instance of the more general case of studying how private determinants of behavior are manifested in public affairs. I was particularly impressed by the fact that the thinking of Dr. Weinstein, whom I had first met in the context of his own study of those who send threatening letters to the President, also inclined toward the more general issue. In fact, he seems to be particularly concerned with the need to develop a methodology for such investigation.[12]

There has been disagreement, even among psychiatrists, about the degree to which psychiatry should become involved in broader social issues, and about how much can be validly inferred about an individual who has not been personally examined by the psychiatrist.* One objection deals with the presumed need for a clinical interview. It is true that the data available about a public figure are not the same as those available from a one to one interview. But, as Weinstein points out,[5] a vast amount of recorded data about such a figure as a President is often available. We can begin to learn how to use the large masses of data which are available. A second objection arises from the fear that psychiatric data might be used to lend an air of

---

*There are indications already that between the time of this meeting and the editing of the papers for publication there has been increasing attention to this aspect by investigators, as I have noted elsewhere(7).

---

*Again, in the interim between presenting this paper and editing it for this publication, it has become clear that psychiatry is moving in the direction of broader social involvement (13,14,15,16). I have also succeeded in interesting two psychiatric residents at Michael Reese Hospital P.&P.I., Drs. Howard Wolin and James Wilson, in doing research in this area.

scientific validity to subjective political views.

In itself, the problem of subjectivity is not insurmountable, nor even entirely objectionable. In dealing with individual patients the psychiatrist has learned not to attempt to eliminate his own emotional reactions to the patient as undesirable countertransference, but to pay attention to his own reactions as a valuable tool in understanding the patient's non-verbal communication.[17, 18] An analogy may be possible in the public sphere.

We may wonder where to start in studying public figures. First of all, we might start off with a simple, probably fairly generally acceptable assumption—that public figures are human beings and thus have human reactions to crises in their life situations.

President Roosevelt had had an extremely serious illness and subsequent physical disability. President Kennedy reportedly almost always had some pain from his back problem.[19] Presidents Eisenhower and Johnson both had histories of heart attacks and both had surgical operations while in office. President Wilson had a stroke while in office. Winston Churchill's medical condition apparently was worse than was publicly revealed.[20] The principal negotiator for the North Vietnamese in Paris, reportedly had leukemia and there was concern over a possible recurrence.[21, 22]

Governor Rockefeller and Governor Stevenson both were divorced. The Mayor of Detroit was having serious marital difficulties at the time his city was torn by riots.[23] Premier Kosygin's wife died shortly before his historic and important meeting with President Johnson in New Jersey.[24] Governor Wallace's wife was operated on for a malignancy and she later died while he was working toward his candidacy for the Presidency—and she was fatally ill herself while governor. President Kennedy lost his new-born child shortly before his assassination.

Governor Rockefeller's son met accidental death while Rockefeller was in office. Senator Percy's daughter was brutally murdered while he was a candidate. Senator Robert Kennedy's brother had been assassinated, as he reminded a group of black people after the assassination of Rev. Dr. Martin Luther King. Senator Edward Kennedy had two brothers who were assassinated. Senators Fulbright and Dirksen lost brothers to natural death.[25, 26]

We would be naive to conclude that these events left no traces whatsoever in the official functioning of these people. Could Premier Kosygin have had no feelings or thoughts whatsoever about his wife's death while he was meeting with President Johnson, or could he have kept those feelings entirely isolated from his participation in the talks? Could there be no effect whatsoever upon the attitude of the North Vietnamese ambassador toward the war he is negotiating, toward killing and death, as a result of possibly having a fatal illness himself?

We know that individuals can react negatively to positive events. They occasionally become depressed paradoxically at times of success, such as, for example, job promotion. Tabachnick *et al.*, in studying fatal one-car accidents, unexpectedly found an improvement in many of the driver-victims' life situations—that they had taken or were about to take a "move forward or upward."[9] Perhaps we also can look to see whether, for example, the winner of an election might react paradoxically to the success of being elected.

We also know that early childhood experiences and the exposure to attitudes of parents are important determinants of later attitudes and personality. It is possible that the exposure of Alexander Dubcek's father to democratic ideals and life in American society and their transmission to the young Alexander did more to foster democracy and fight Communism than a good many projects we plan and initiate for that purpose.[27] Some of these, such as the Vietnam war, probably exert such a disrupting psychological effect on children as to make a whole generation less capable of governing itself in the future.[28, 29, 30]

Although we have taken a few steps, we do not fully know how to approach the psychiatric study of public figures; the working out of useful methods should have a high priority. It would be of great value if we could learn whether and how unconscious factors might frustrate and sabotage the conscious intentions of a leader—why it was, for example, that President Wilson, who was able to conceive and formulate such a brilliant and creative plan for the post World War I era, was able to put so little of it into effect.

My own effort—in applying the results from the threateners to the study of Oswald, and in considering the psychology of Presidents and other leaders, including the comments above about life crises—has been to apply psychodynamic psychiatry to the information available about the public behavior and public expressions of these individuals, *as if* it were obtained from them directly, and to see whether it can begin to fit together into a coherent pattern for a person in that role in which we are interested.

In the case of Oswald, my aim was to gain an understanding of Oswald in his role as the assassin of a President. This is not necessarily a picture of him in every area of his functioning as an entire human being. In studying Presidents or other leaders, the aim would be to develop a picture of the President in his role as President, not necessarily a picture of him in all areas of his personal private functioning, so we would not be unduly disappointed by the fact that our raw material was incomplete, that the statements made might have been influenced by the need to present a certain image to the public, might not be entirely frank and candid in all instances.

We well know that to some extent any picture is influenced by circumstances in which we obtain it. When we treat a patient, we realize that we are seeing only one aspect and basing our formulations upon that aspect visible to us. When we study a public figure we can also keep in mind that we are seeing only one aspect of the person and basing our formulations upon that aspect.

We are aware of the "information threshold," so to speak, between what is unconscious and what is conscious. There is a drastic attenuation and restructuring of information into organized patterns as material goes from unconscious to conscious.[31] So too, is there an "information threshold" between what is conscious but intrapsychic and what is communicated interpersonally, with a corresponding attenuation and restructuring of information into organized patterns.[31]

In all of our daily lives we extrapolate back from what is interpersonally communicated to infer what the communicator is consciously aware of, what the conscious determinants of the message are. In our daily professional lives we extrapolate even further back to get some idea of what the patient is not consciously aware of, what the unconscious determinants of the message are.

We may now postulate an additional "information threshold" between what is ordinarily communicated interpersonally and what is communicated publicly, "for the record." There is an attenuation and restructuring of information into new patterns "for the record." Even in our role as citizens we are always trying to extrapolate backwards from what is "for the record." It is now proposed to add our psychiatric skills in our efforts to extrapolate back over this information threshold to arrive at implicit determinants.

Thus we have a new concept to add to the constructs of the various *intrapsychic* levels, such as unconscious, conscious, etc.—an analogous concept of more than one level of *extrapsychic* function, a construct of a public figure in his role as a public figure, "for the record," as distinct from his interpersonal functioning "off the record." For this reason, psychiatric conclusions about a public figure will be descriptions of the *hypothetical construct* of that person in his *role as a public figure*.

Even though they may often *sound* similar to descriptions of a patient, they cannot be equated. Perhaps some new terminology will need to be invented to maintain the distinctions. The descriptions of the hypothetical construct will carry no implications for other areas of that person's life, no connotations of moral judgment, blame or praise, and will make no argument for any clinical psychiatric intervention, such as treatment or hospitalization.

They will not mean that he was, or is a good person, or a bad person. They will not even mean that he was, or is, mentally ill, mentally healthy, "fit," or "unfit," in need of, or not in need of, mental hospitalization, etc.

A concrete approximation to this concept of extrapsychic levels, which can serve as a useful illustration at this point, is found in a recent paper on de Gaulle.[32]

The authors refer to Malraux's concept of "a *dedoublement* of de Gaulle— the man and the personage", and suggest even "a *detriplement:* There is *Charles* [the private person]; there is the public-political *de Gaulle,* the temporal leader, who happens to be . . . President; and there is the public historic person, the embodiment of France's cause, *General de Gaulle . . .*"

They speak of *Charles'* relation to his *public* self as that of an artist to his creation. Referring to the distinction between the private and public aspects, they comment that, "It is as if there were two parallel de Gaulles. . . . The personality that is spread over the map is the *public* personage, not the private self . . ."

Editing this paper for publication has made necessary a great deal of condensation and elimination of details and examples. I have attempted to focus more upon the methodology in the context of this scientific publication, and to cover the historical examples elsewhere.[6, 7] However, it seems in order to outline the direction in which the findings seem to be leading at this point, and to indicate some of the observations which show the way.

As we begin to look into the question of whether there might be factors in the personalities of Presidents and other leaders in general, or certain particular Presidents or leaders, which might make them more prone to assassination—whether there may be anything akin to the idea of subintentional death in accident victims or victims of aggression—there do appear to be some indications in the observable behavior of these leaders of what one might view as unconscious fantasies of omnipotence or counterphobic elements aimed at mastering man's mortality. These could inadvertently elicit the very fate which they seek to master.

In one way, this could be viewed as evidence for an unrealistic belief in their own indestructibility which would allow them to take unwarranted risks, unwarranted because the leaders remain, after all, mortal men. It even appears in some cases as if there may be a tendency to take a risk for the sake of the risk—to challenge or dare death—combined with an air of fatalism. All of this would both mask and reveal an underlying fascination with death.

The tendency to take risks may show up in such apparently innocuous behavior as driving a car. Sorensen comments on John Kennedy's dangerously fast driving as a Senator, driving such that an aide refused to ride in the right front "death seat", a position Sorensen accepted only for fear that if he (Sorensen) rode in the back seat, "the Senator would turn around as he drove."[19]

Frank Wilson, the Secret Service Chief for President Roosevelt (F.D.R.), relates an incident when Roosevelt took him for a spin around Hyde Park, taking pleasure in scaring Wilson. Wilson relates that Roosevelt's driving was always a worry to him. "He often took his eyes off the road and his hand off the wheel in order to wave to people."[33]

The tendency to take risks may show in ways more closely connected with the Presidential office. The Warren Commission Report recognized that many Presidents have been impatient with security precautions.[34] Presidents have been known to take pleasure in eluding Secret Service protection.

Wilson, concerned about Roosevelt's driving, first tried to convince F.D.R. to watch the road, considered putting a governor on the engine, and finally decided to have agents cut off side roads and send pilot cars ahead of and behind the President. This merely provided Roosevelt with a "new game", to ditch the pilot drivers. Reaching home after a successful attempt, he "grinned impishly" at Wilson and teased him that his agents had "disappeared".[33]

Writing in 1962, just after retiring as Secret Service Chief, U. E. Baughman is both admiring and critical of "the utter disregard for his own personal safety" which Richard Nixon showed as Vice President.[35] He quotes one of his agents, who had watched Nixon rush toward a disorderly crowd, as saying that Nixon had "delusions of personal safety".

Baughman had come to think of Nixon as "an assassin's delight, a murderer's dreamboat," with respect to his indifference to his own safety and the Secret Service's efforts to protect him. Baughman also considered John Kennedy, like Nixon, to be "incorrigibly brave" and utterly indifferent to his own physical safety.

John Kennedy and his brothers were known to be brave, and to take risks. At Harvard, young Jack, while ill with a high fever, nightly sneaked out of the infirmary to practice for a place on the swimming team.[36] Robert Kennedy was quoted as telling his children, in a pep talk, that "A Kennedy shouldn't be scared." Reportedly he had continued playing in a football game until he collapsed and it was discovered that he had broken his leg in an earlier play.[36]

Jack and Joe, Jr., to "prove" that the wind and water were not too rough to proceed with a regatta, startled visiting sailors by heading out to sea in their boat, fell overboard, swam through the waves to the empty sailboat, and returned to the dock.[36] Both Joe, Jr. and Jack joined the Navy, although Jack had to make three attempts to get into the service, having been turned down once by the Navy and once by the Army because of his spinal injury.[36, 37]

Jack pulled strings to get into combat duty and his bravery in the PT boat incident is well known. Joe, Jr. had turned down orders to return to Stateside duty in order to volunteer for the hazardous mission in which he was killed. His baggage was already loaded aboard the New York-bound transport ship when he volunteered for the risky mission.[36, 38]

If a deeper fascination with death underlies an effort too master it by counterphobic means, this fascination may also show up in a fatalistic attitude. Weisz and Taylor discuss the fatalistic stance of victims such as Lincoln, Garfield, and both Kennedys.[39] Lincoln several times returned to the White House with bullet holes in his hat after unescorted rides at night.

Greening has discussed the increase in risk-taking behavior on the part of Robert Kennedy which occurred after his brother John's assassination.[40] Greening quotes *Time* correspondent Hugh Sidey's remembrance that, "There was in those days [after Dallas] . . . a sense of urgency about him, almost as if he were sliding toward some faraway disaster. . . . That is when he began to shoot rapids and climb mountains," having, what *Time* described as "an almost existential need to dare the elements," which included a plunge into piranha infested waters while on a canoe trip down the Amazon.[41] In that same issue of *Time*, it is commented that, "Robert Kennedy had long felt the possibility that some day people would no longer be able to mention 'the Kennedy assassination' without specifying which one."[42]

As Theodore Sorensen describes John Kennedy, "Under that seemingly fortunate and gay exterior lay an acute awareness of the most sobering kinds of tragedy. He lived with the memory of a much admired older brother killed in the war and the memory of a sister killed in a plane crash overseas."[19]

Schlesinger tells how John Kennedy loved to hear Jacqueline recite his favorite poem, Alan Seeger's "I Have a Rendezvous with Death."[43] Martin Luther King, Jr. delivered the eulogy at his own funeral.

So, we can view the behavior of these people as revealing unconscious fantasies of omnipotence, counterphobic elements, and fatalism. But it all depends on how we structure our conceptualization. We might also view the behavior as heroic. It might indicate that the leader *has* come to terms with and accepts his own mortality. In fact, the very same attribute which could be viewed as unrealistic in one light might be viewed as an important factor leading to success.

It appears that a successful leader may have to be an individual who acts as if he is, and perhaps in some ways believes himself to be, incapable of failure, assured of success. This assurance of success may have to be communicated to the public non-verbally by confident action. Thus, the same attitude which conveys confidence to the public may make safety more difficult.[33]

The dual nature of this may be illustrated by Winston Churchill's trips across the North Atlantic to enlist our support early in World War II. He made the trips despite danger from German submarines, a danger which could not be completely eliminated despite secrecy and other precautions.[44] Had his ship been sunk it would have been disastrous. In fact, the ship used on his summer, 1941 trip was sunk shortly before the December, 1941 trip.[44] A more prudent man might have stayed in safety. Perhaps it took someone with an unrealistic faith in his own indestructibility to do this. Yet it was no doubt this very faith in ultimate success which made him a great leader, rallied public support, morale, and enthusiasm, and gave the British people the faith in themselves to fight on.

Apparently other psychiatrists also have perceived something of this in Churchill. In three separate instances when I discussed this idea with colleagues they responded by mentioning a paper by Kohut[45] which makes a somewhat similar observation about a possible unconscious grandiose fantasy, less well integrated, in Churchill's earlier life. In a more recent book, another psychiatrist also comes to somewhat similar conclusions about Churchill.[46]

Baughman balances his negative comments about Richard Nixon's indifference to his physical safety with a comment that to be physically fearless seems to be a condition of greatness, that it allows such men to take action under circumstances which could paralyze other men.[35]

Hoffmann and Hoffmann indicate that one ingredient of de Gaulle's charisma is the ability to call upon millenial hopes of rescue which arise in the depths of national crisis and despair; that *under circumstances of extreme and irremediable disaster,* he could appear as "the prophet, the unifier, the remover of the roadblocks. . . ."[32]

I did not take my thoughts about the possibility of "assassination proneness" seriously enough to keep me from being shocked and surprised by the assassination of Senator Robert Kennedy, but it did seem to be a sad confirmation of the idea I already had. As I edit this, just as the first men have landed on the moon in a culmination of President Kennedy's space program, the almost simultaneous news of his one remaining brother's auto accident uncannily reminds me of the unanticipated finding in the one car accident study concerning a recent or impending "move forward or upward."[9]

The study of assassination has led me to a concern about the importance of a President's attitude toward death. But a President's attitude toward death has been pointed out to be a factor in another even more serious area, that of war.[47] The imminent threat of nuclear destruction makes it imperative that we understand as much as possible about all factors which might influence its realization.

Weinstein points out that the tragedy of *Wilson's* life was that the very qualities in him which had been the source of his greatness became the agents of his political disaster.[5] Hoffman and Hoffmann point out the necessity for national disaster to have happened in order for *de Gaulle* to be the voice of hope and effort, to call up millenial hopes of rescue.[32]

Perhaps psychiatry can begin to understand the sources of greatness and disaster so that our leaders may be more assured of directing their courses to reach their consciously intended goals, so that disaster does not have to be an antecedent or a consequence of their greatness.

If psychiatry can begin to elucidate previously unrecognized factors which go into making decisions as to what is and is not reasonable in the public sphere, as it does in the private sphere with our patients, it may make as significant a contribution to freedom and democracy in the public sphere as it makes on the individual level toward our patients' freedom from irrational forces. It may contribute not only to our Presidents' survival from potential assassination; it may contribute to our species' survival.

REFERENCES

1. Rothstein, David A.: Presidential Assassination Syndrome. *Arch. Gen. Psychiat.* 11:245-254, (Sept.) 1964.
2. Rothstein, David A.: Presidential Assassination Syndrome: II. Application to Lee Harvey Oswald. *Arch. Gen. Psychiat.* 15:260-266, (Sept.) 1966.
3. Meeting with members of President's Commission on the Assassination of President Kennedy (Warren Commission), Commission Staff, and psychiatrists, Washington, D. C., July 9, 1964.
4. Rothstein, David A.: Testimony at Hearing of National Commission on the Causes and Prevention of Violence (Eisenhower Commission), Task Force on Political Assassination. Washington, D. C., Oct. 3, 1968.
5. Weinstein, Edwin A.: Denial of Presidential Disability: A Case Study of Woodrow Wilson. *Psychiatry*, 30:376-391, (Nov.) 1967.
6. Rothstein, David A.: *Presidential Assassination Syndrome;* Englewood Cliffs: Prentice-Hall (in press).
7. Rothstein, David A.: Presidential Assassination Syndrome: A Psychiatric Study of the Threat, the Deed, and the Message, in *Assassinations and the Political Order,* Crotty, W. J., ed. New York: Harper and Row (in press).
8. Macdonald, John M.: *The Murderer and His Victim.* Springfield, Ill.: C. C. Thomas, 1961.
9. Tabachnick, Norman, *et al.*: Comparative Psychiatric Study of Accidental and Suicidal Death. *Arch. Gen. Psychiat.* 14:60-68, (Jan.) 1966.

10. Litman, Robert E., and Tachnick, Norman: Fatal One-Car Accidents. *Psychoanal. Quart.* 36:248-259, (April) 1967.

11. Shneidman, Edwin S.: Orientations Toward Death: A Vital Aspect of the Study of Lives. *Internat. J. Psychiat.* 2:167-188, (March) 1966.

12. Weinstein, Edwin: Personal Communication (letter), March 4, 1968.

13. Rome, Howard P.: Psychiatry and Foreign Affairs: The Expanding Competence of Psychiatry, *Amer. J. Psychiat.* 125:725-730, (Dec.) 1968.

14. Wedge, Bryant: Training for a Psychiatry of International Relations. *Amer. J. Psychiat.* 125:731-736, (Dec.) 1968.

15. Special Section. Private Conflict with Public Consequences. *Amer. J. Psychiat.* 125:1074-1107. (Feb.) 1969.

16. Waggoner, Raymond W.: A More Active Role for Psychiatrists (Editorial). *Amer. J. Psychiat.* 125:1108-1109 (Feb.) 1969.

17. Searles, Harold F.: The Schizophrenic Individual's Experience of His World. *Psychiatry.* 30:119-131. (May) 1967.

18. Fleming, Joan, and Benedek, Therese: *Psychoanalytic Supervision.* New York: Grune and Stratton, 1966.

19. Sorensen, Theodore: *Kennedy.* New York: Harper and Row, 1965.

20. Robitscher, Jonas: Doctors' Privileged Communications, Public Life, and History's Rights. *Cleveland-Marshall Law Review.* 17:199-212, (May) 1968.

21. Ghali, Paul: Hanoi Hints Quitting Talks. *Chicago Daily News.* Fri. July 26, 1968, p. 1.

22. Ghali, Paul: Personal communication (letter), Nov. 15, 1968.

23. Cavanaghs trade charges. *Chicago Daily News.* Wed., July 17, 1968. p. 6.

24. Aleksei Kosygin: The Compleat *Apparatchik. Time.* 89:13 (June 30) 1967.

25. Milestones. *Time.* 91:89, (March 15) 1968.

26. Milestones. *Time.* 91:80, (March 22) 1968.

27. Dubcek's father lived in Chicago. *Chicago Daily News.* Mon., Aug. 12, 1968, p. 2.

28. Wangh, Martin: A Psychogenetic Factor in the Recurrence of War. *Int. J. Psycho-Anal.* 49:319-323, (parts 2-3) 1968.

29. Anderson, Robert E.: Where's Dad? Paternal Deprivation and Delinquency. *Arch. Gen. Psychiat.* 18:641-649, (June) 1968.

30. Trunnell, Thomas L.: The Absent Father's Children's Emotional Disturbances. *Arch. Gen. Psychiat.* 19:180-188, (Aug.) 1968.

31. Rothstein, David A.: Psychiatric Implications of Information Theory. *Arch. Gen. Psychiat.* 13:87-94. (July) 1965.

32. Hoffman, Stanley, and Hoffman, Inge: The Will to Grandeur: de Gaulle as Political Artist. *Daedalus* 97:829-887, (Summer) 1968.

33. Wilson, Frank J. and Day, Beth: *Special Agent.* New York: Holt, Rinehart and Winston, 1965.

34. *Report of the President's Commission on the Assassination of President Kennedy (Warren Commission).* Washington: U.S. Government Printing Office, 1964.

35. Baughman, U.E., with Robinson, L. W.: *Secret Service Chief.* New York: Harper and Row, 1962.

36. McCarthy, Joe: The Remarkable Kennedys. New York: Popular Library, 1960.

37. Whalen, Richard J.: *The Founding Father. The Story of Joseph P. Kennedy.* New York: New American Library, 1966.

38. Olsen, Jack: *Aphrodite: Desperate Mission.* New York: G. P. Putnam's Sons, 1970.

39. Weisz, Alfred, and Taylor, Robert: The Assassination Matrix. *Stanford Today.* Winter, 1969, p. 11-17.

40. Greening, Thomas: The Psychological Study of Assassins. in *Assassinations and the Political Order,* Crotty, W. J., ed. New York: Harper and Row (in press).

41. *Time.* 91:19 (June 14), 1968.

42. *Time.* 91:16-18 (June 14), 1968.

43. Schlesinger, Arthur M., Jr.: *A Thousand Days. John F. Kennedy in the White House.* Cambridge: Riverside Press, 1965.
44. Churchill, Winston: *The Grand Alliance.* New York: Bantam Books, 1962.
45. Kohut, Heinz: Forms and Transformations of Narcissism. *J. Amer. Psychoanal. Assn.* 14:243-272, (April) 1966.
46. Taylor, A. J. P., James, R. R., Plum, J. H., Hart, B. L. and Storr, A.: *Churchill Revised.* New York: Dial, 1969.
47. Mintz, Ira L.: Unconscious Motives in the Making of War. *Medical Opinion and Review* 4:88-95, (April) 1968.

VIOLENT BEHAVIOR IN PRISONS

Augustus F. Kinzel, M.D.

During a panel discussion of "the clinical evaluation of the dangerousness of the mentally ill" at the 1965 annual meeting of the American Psychiatric Association, the following case was described as very perplexing:

Willy was serving a sentence for a misdemeanor. During the confinement he was unduly sensitive to physical contact with other males, and, as a result, was involved in fist fights. Within four days of his release . . . he slashed seven strangers in broad daylight . . . and there were four deaths . . . in Matteawan . . . he didn't do anything aggressive except that he was just sensitive to homosexual approach . . . .[1]

This case, and many more like it, make psychiatrists appear, at first glance, as if they are just as ignorant in understanding, identifying and predicting violent behavior as prison staffs, courts and, the American public often think they are.

Rubin, counsel for the National Council on Crime and Delinquency, makes the challenging statement, ". . . psychiatry today does not have the requisite knowledge for a screening procedure to determine who is dangerous on a broad scale."[2] Although they do not have an accurate screening procedure, psychiatrists definitely do use criteria derived from direct clinical experience.

Perhaps the more cogent questions to ask are: what criteria do psychiatrists use, how reliable are they, and in what areas are psychiatrists, indeed, relatively ignorant?

As staff psychiatrist on the maximum security unit at the U. S. Medical Center for Federal Prisoners, I was confronted by these questions in my daily work. I quickly discovered that, although I was familiar with violence as a manifestation of the acute psychoses, I knew little about what triggered violence—instead of withdrawal or flight—in psychotic individuals. With non-psychotics, I was even less informed. I had some idea that socio-

---

Dr. Kinzel is instructor in psychiatry in the College of Physicians and Surgeons, Columbia University, New York, New York.

pathic individuals tended to be aggressive because they lacked conscience, were impulsive, or were brought up that way. I had no knowledge, however, of the psychodynamics of their violent behavior. Movies and the press had led me to believe that inmates were invariably violent when someone broke their strict social code by "ratting" or "snitching." In my daily clinical work, however, I could readily see that such behavior was not a common cause of violence.

In an attempt to separate fact from fiction, I became a regular consultant to the prison discipline committee. There I was able to interview enough violent prisoners, from the psychiatric, medical, surgical and prison camp inmate groups, to begin to see some emerging patterns of violence that were somewhat surprising and not immediately understandable. These observations prompted the following study:

Thirty-six consecutive incidents of fighting, assault with and without a weapon, and attempted murder reported to the discipline committee were investigated by direct interview of both the aggressor and the victim, by reports of staff observers, and by review of criminal records.

The particular focus was on the immediate precipitating event, or that situation or condition which appeared most directly to trigger the violent behavior. The results are summarized in Table 1.

Table 1: IMMEDIATE TRIGGERS OF VIOLENT INCIDENTS

Acute psychosis	10
Homosexuality	6
Property infringement	5
Inappropriate command	5
Accidental contact	3
Horseplay	2
Infringement of privacy	2
Inappropriate personal comment	2
Racial animosity	1
TOTAL	36

In the acute psychotics, violent behavior appeared to erupt much more often from within the individual rather than from provocation from the external environment. Several inmates appeared to "run amok" in acute catatonic excitement; others lashed out ineffectively in acute toxic psychoses; the remainder, being acutely delusional, struck out at bystanders who they imagined were persecuting them. More often than not, the aggressors were unknown to the victims. The aggressors, however, often insisted they were attacking because of the victims' provocations.

Although they rarely could state clearly what the provocations were, they frequently used such expressions as "he was eye-balling me," "he was getting up in my face," or "he was messing with my mind." The statements seemed to indicate that the psychotic aggressors thought they perceived some real threat to their physical integrity from their victims, while, to other observers, the victims appeared to have done nothing provocative.

The most severe violence was committed by homosexual inmates caught up in intense, jealous competition for a sexual partner. In these cases, one, two, or all three of those involved in the homosexual triangle showed intense, rapidly alternating, ambivalent feelings and behavior prior to the incident. Their violence appeared to express both the intense wish for possession and the intense wish for destruction of the desired sexual object.

It was not usually immediately apparent that a triangle was involved, and often extensive interviewing and collecting of staff observations were required to reveal it. In the remaining homosexual cases, pairs fought when one attempted to "break up." In one case, indiscriminate propositioning of a non-homosexual inmate led to a violent assault.

Stealing or unpaid debts were property infringements that provoked some violence. In several instances, however, the infringement was trivial, such as sitting in the aggressor's chair by accident.

Some inmates given temporary responsibility over other inmates began abusing their power, and started to give commands quite liberally. The responsibility appeared to "go to their head."

Several inmates appeared to be particularly sensitive to the sudden intrusion of another person, even when accidental. Touching another person and backing into another in line provoked violence. Even a misthrown basketball, not causing injury, provoked a violent assault. Inmates, apparently enjoying back-slapping, sham punching and teasing, suddenly attacked, demonstrating a sudden sensitivity to being touched.

"Ratting" or "snitching" provoked relatively little violence—and no more so than did "making too much noise." Comments such as "you look sick," "you've got dandruff," or "you ought to go to church," were apparently sufficient to provoke violence. Racial animosity accounted for the least amount of violence.

This survey suggested that violent behavior and homosexuality in prison inmates might be much more interrelated than is generally recognized. The most striking and surprising findings were the extreme sensitivity to close relationships, to being touched, to personal comments, and the tendency to perceive passive or accidental intrusion as an active threat to physical integrity.

The obvious explanation of this was that the Medical Center had an inordinate number of psychotics and homosexuals.

It was found, however, that over half of the psychotics were sent from other prisons not because they were psychotic but because they were violent, while all of the non-psychotics were sent because of their violent or disruptive behavior. They were simply repeating such behavior at the new institution.

A spot check at a regular Federal prison of comparable size revealed exactly the same percentage of violent incidents as at the Medical Center. Sixteen percent of reported incidents involved violence in both institutions over the same nine-month period. Although not verified, the impression was that the patterns of violence at the Medical Center were not substantially different from those found in regular prisons.

Diagnosis of the non-psychotics, who predominated in the group surveyed, was extremely difficult. The most typical psychopathology consisted of periodic abrupt breakthroughs of perceptual distortions and violence, followed by long periods characterized chiefly by sociopathic characterological difficulties. Usually the violent episode was quickly denied, and later, if acknowledged at all, the degree of violence that had been involved was invariably minimized.

It was extremely difficult to arrive at a reliable estimate of the proportion of this violent group to the total prison population. Conrad states that 0.6 percent of the California prison population are violent while in prison.[3]

But there is so much variability in the reporting of violent incidents, that official figures are open to question. A study by Wolf[4] showed quite clearly that correctional staffs rated offenses such as escape, possession of a weapon, intoxication with drugs or alcohol, sexual perversion, destruction of government property, and refusal to obey as "more serious" than assault on another inmate. What an officer may call "just a fight" is frequently a serious assault, but often it is not reported as such.

At the Medical Center, a rough estimate based on official as well as grapevine reports indicated that aside from riots, roughly 5 per cent of the inmate population were violent in prison. This incidence is still far lower than is generally believed.

Because those who were violent virtually dictated the atmosphere, the policies and the focus of attention of the entire institution, a further investigation was undertaken to define the differentiating characteristics of the violent group. From a total of 25 screened, the eight prisoners with histories of the most frequent violent behavior were compared to the six prisoners with histories of the least frequent violent behavior.

The violent prisoners were chosen from those reported for fighting or assault in 1967. The non-violent subjects were chosen from those living on a minimum security unit during the same period. The information was obtained by psychiatric interview, and review of criminal records. In the interview, inquiries were made about 26 factors known or believed to be associated with violent behavior. The characteristics listed in Table 2 appeared best to differentiate the violent from the non-violent group.

Table 2: DIFFERENTIATING CHARACTERISTICS OF THE VIOLENT GROUP

Repeated violent behavior with little provocation
Frequent necessity for forceable restraint
Fighting with a weapon
Carrying a weapon for prolonged periods "for protection"
History of violence between parents
Serious accidents (self-perpetrated)
Bisexuality and hypersexuality
Hypersensitivity to name calling
History of violence to domestic animals

All of the prisoners in the violent group gave a history of repeated violent behavior where the provocations usually were not physical threats. The extent of the history of violence reported in the interview was often much greater than the amount recorded in pre-sentence investigations, classification studies and arrest records.

One inmate insisted he had one unfriendly fight almost every day from the first to the seventh grade. The only related comment in his record was ". . . inmate had some adjustment problems at school." Two of the eight revealed murders that were nowhere recorded. Although they offered this information somewhat hesitatingly, it was not difficult to elicit. These men gave the impression that no one had ever asked them if they had killed anyone.

The frequency of violence in this group was quite variable. A rough average was two to five assaults per year. They tended to be much more violent without accomplices than with. They all recalled friends or police pulling them off someone, and a few sensed that, unlike their friends, they often didn't know when to stop and had to be restrained.

Most had habitually carried a knife or a gun, claiming it made them feel better, or more "protected." They tended to deny any desire to use the weapon on others, but many admitted actually having done so. None gave histories of being severely beaten in childhood, although all gave histories of violence between their parents. It was not possible to determine whether parental violence was more frequent in the violent than in the non-violent group. Accidents with cars, weapons and fires were common, and often led to injury. Banging fists through windows and almost intentional self-cutting were surprisingly frequent.

Seven of eight gave a history of infrequent homosexual contacts both in and out of prisons, yet all denied they were homosexuals, claiming they took the male role, and did not do it so much for the pleasure as for the money or other benefits that might accrue.

Some indicated that when they had been asked to take the feminine role, they actually assaulted the other individual. They tended to want heterosexual intercourse as often as possible when out of prison, but claimed they did not particularly miss it when in prison. When they could find a woman, they tended to want to have intercourse several times without interruption. However, relationships with women were usually quite short lived.

Being called names such as "M-F," "punk," or "S.O.B." was often in itself enough to provoke violent assault. All except one gave a history of several instances of cruelty to cats and dogs by burning, drowning, or mutilating.

Also quite striking, but more difficult to assess, was the relative absence of fantasy in these men. They did not seem to dream, daydream, or attach much value to thought. Instead, they seemed to express themselves by body action almost exclusively. It was particularly striking that, although they spoke relatively freely about their violent pasts, they almost totally denied their own aggressiveness, so that none actually considered himself a violent individual.

The characteristics discussed were found least frequently in the non-violent group. None had a frequency of violence greater than three or four incidents since puberty, and most of these involved little injury and a good deal of provocation.

The impression was gained from interviewing prisoners classified in the violent group that most of the characteristics differentiating them from the non-violent group stemmed from pre-adolescence, and that, although they were all chronologically adults, most of them were still functioning at the level of the competitive, homosexual, peer and authority conflicts that characterize the latency period in normal development.

Of particular note was their extreme sensitivity to physical closeness and to threats of homosexual submission. Above all other factors, these two seemed to be most closely related to their invariable feeling that they were attacking others in self-defense. Therefore, a further procedure was devised to try to measure how sensitive these violent individuals actually were to non-threatening physical closeness.

Horowitz identified an area surrounding the body, within which anxiety is produced if another person enters.[5] He defined this "body-buffer zone" as ". . . an area surrounding each individual which represents the boundaries to what is felt as 'inner' versus what is felt as 'outer'." He found that such an area could be measured experimentally. This concept showed promise in elucidating the apparent hypersensitivity to physical closeness in the violent prisoners.

Each of the eight violent and six non-violent prisoners, mentioned in the previous study, was asked to stand in the center of a 20 x 20 ft. bare room. Standing eight feet in front of the subject, the experimenter, wearing a white coat and known to the subject as a physician, told the subject that he would slowly approach him, and instructed him to say "stop" when he felt that the experimenter had come "too close."

At the point where the subject said "stop," the experimenter recorded the distance between his toes and the center of the room where the subject was standing. When he made similar approaches from the rear of the subject, the experimenter instructed the subject to turn his head and look, but not to turn his trunk. The area within the eight closest distances tolerated by the subject was identified as the body-buffer zone. This procedure was repeated weekly on each subject for 12 weeks.

The average body-buffer zones of the violent group were almost four (3.8) times larger than the zones of the non-violent group. In addition, the rear zones were significantly larger than the front zones for the violent group. That is, the violent subjects kept the experimenter at further distances when he approached from behind than when he approached from the front.

By contrast the front zones tended to be larger than the rear zones for the non-violent group.

Although both groups tolerated the experimenter at closer distances by the end of the 12 weekly determinations, the differences between the groups remained significant, even though by that time the experimenter was clearly perceived more as friend than foe.

The subjects' comments following the procedures were quite revealing of their hypersensitivity to mere physical proximity. Several of the violent group felt shivers or "goosepimples" across their shoulders and down their backs, when the experimenter approached from the rear. Many also indicated that, when the experimenter had slowly entered their zone thresholds, he seemed to be "looming" or "rushing in" at them. Many recalled similar sensations prior to violent incidents.

A more rigorous double blind technique and a physiological means of measuring the zone threshold will be necessary to validate these findings. It is possible that zone measurement alone might have some value as a screening procedure in identifying and predicting a potential for violence.[6] It is further possible that an expanding body-buffer zone might precede a violent outburst.

The findings strongly point to the importance of homosexual anxiety as the crucial trigger of violent behavior in the individuals studied. The transient violent outbursts of both psychotic and non-psychotic prisoners appeared to result from a rapid protection of the sudden impending breakthrough of intolerable, passive, homosexual desires. Such desires were then quickly re-repressed following the violent outburst.

Kempf, in 1926, stated: "The mechanism of homosexual panic is of utmost importance wherever men or women must be grouped alone for prolonged periods, as in army camps, aboard ships, in prisons, monasteries, schools and asylums."[7] To this important statement I can only add that the tendency toward homosexual panic may account for violence outside of prison as well as inside, in those individuals who perceive *any* physical closeness as a threatening confinement.

This tendency may be of crucial importance in the aggressive, violent individual, as well as in the passive, weak individual. It may appear as momentary violent outbursts instead of prolonged delusional states, and may be present in any diagnostic category.

In summary, the data presented here although by no means conclusive, offers some additional information about violence in individuals that, if pursued, might help identify and evaluate the potential for violence. This study of violence in prisoners suggests that individuals predisposed to violence comprise a much smaller proportion of those incarcerated than is usually recognized, that the frequency of their violence, however, is much greater than is usually recognized, and that their outbursts are more liable to be transient and intermittent rather than prolonged.

This study also suggests that they appear most threatened by emotional and physical closeness, that their tendency toward homosexual panic is much greater than it appears, and that their violent behavior is frequently representative of a disorder present as far back as the pre-adolescent period. Routine incarceration may have little effect on the frequency of their violence, and certainly does not stop it. Measures such as the body-buffer zone might reveal specific characteristics of violent individuals that could lead to practical screening devices.

Until rigorous studies with large samples are undertaken to further define the unique characteristics of violent individuals, psychiatrists will continue to have to work with intuitions of questionable reliability, in making decisions that are often of life and death importance. Sharpening skills in this area should be the first order of business in any prison, parole, hospital, community psychiatry or judicial program.

It is quite possible that should such skills become truly refined, we might be able to provide not only truly effective treatment facilities for violent individuals, but also to free from incarceration much greater numbers who are not likely to be violent.

Returning to the case of Willy, we might now wonder how many "fist fights" Willy actually was involved in, both in and out of institutions, and why in the face of these violent incidents he was considered as not doing "anything aggressive?" Wasn't Willy's sensitivity "to homosexual approach" really crucial evidence of his tendency toward homosexual panic, instead of "just" an incidental quirk?

And if we could have measured it, wouldn't his body-buffer zone have been so large as to have alerted us to his potential for violence and homosexual anxiety? In answering these questions couldn't we have spared four lives as well as Willy's life?

REFERENCES

1. Rappeport, Jonas R.: *The Clinical Evaluation of the Dangerousness of the Mentally Ill*, Charles C. Thomas, Springfield, Illinois, 1967.
2. Rubin, Sol: Int J Psychiat, Vol. 6, No. 3:217, 1968.
3. Conrad, John P.: The Annals of the Am Acad of Pol and Soc Science; Vol. 364, 1966.
4. Wolf, S., Friniek, W.R., Shaffer, J.W.: J Clin Psychol 22:244, 1966.
5. Horowitz, M.J., Duff, D.F., and Stratton, L.O.: Arch Gen Psychiat 11:65, 1964.
6. Kinzel, A.F.: Amer J Psychiat 127:1, 99-104, July, 1970.
7. Kempf, E.J.: *Psychopathology*, C. V. Mosby Co., St. Louis, Mo., pp 477, 1926.

THE ROLE OF GENIC ACTIVITY IN THE DETERMINATION OF SENSITIVE PERIODS IN THE DEVELOPMENT OF AGGRESSIVE BEHAVIOR *

Benson E. Ginsburg, Ph.D.

Psychiatrists and geneticists have been carrying on an ambivalent flirtation for many years. Whatever the prevailing orientation, man has a "nature," "capacities," "tendencies," "instincts," "drives," that arise from his biological substratum. He is not infinitely malleable, although it is often convenient to consider that unless he has been the victim of a sinister biological accident, such as cretinism, trisomy-21, or an extra Y-chromosome, experiential factors predominate in shaping his later behavior.

This view is, after all, the foundation upon which rests the hope that the manipulation of behavior and the reinterpretation of experience may produce therapeutic results. The hope has been bolstered by animal studies, in which it has been shown that early deprivation and the programming of particular kinds of experiences at certain sensitive stages of an animal's life history will profoundly alter its later behavior, thus providing a causal hypothesis for behavioral aberrations that can be produced in this way, as well as a basis for an analogy to emotional and non-ideational behavior in man.[1, 2, 3, 4, 5]

The aforesaid view also receives support from operant conditioning experiments in which motor components can be repatterned into behavioral sequences that are not typical of the species. The picture that often emerges from a synthesis of such researches is that variations from the norms in

*The researches reported in this paper were supported by NIMH grant MH-03361 and by a grant from the Illinois State Department of Mental Health (Psychiatric Training and Research Fund #17-302).

The results reported in this paper include those of the author and of J. S. Cowen, J. E. Jumonville, S. C. Maxson and P. Y. Sze of the Behavior Genetics Laboratory, formerly at the University of Chicago and now at the University of Connecticut.

Dr. Ginsburg is professor and head of the Department of Biobehavioral Sciences, University of Connecticut, Storrs.

individual and social behavior may be attributed to experiential factors and may be altered therapeutically by manipulating further experience. Hereditary variables operate in the broad sense to determine the potential that a species has for assimilating and reacting to environmental factors, and in the narrow sense to restrict this potential—in the extreme case, through some biological malfunction.

Animal and human studies are further conjoined by evolutionary considerations as these are used to interpret behavior in a comparative context over time. Darwin developed and applied this approach to behavior in his book, "The Expression of the Emotions in Man and Animals".

More recently, but in the same tradition, the school of animal behavior research that calls itself "ethology" has sought a methodology for the description and analysis of behavior that would permit us to understand what its biological components are and what its course of evolution has been.

Where the morphologist has structures to compare, both ontogenetically and phylogenetically, the ethologist has turned to movements and motor patterns, and has analyzed these from the point of view of phyletic homologies, origins and sequence in development, and adaptive value under natural conditions.

The problem of what is "innate" or pre-programmed in the genes has been approached by ethologists by a comparison of behavior analyzed in these terms under natural conditions as contrasted with artificial restrictions and manipulations during development. Many of these latter studies are, in one way or another, deprivation experiments. The behaviors that ethologists select for study are those considered to be characteristic of an entire species. These are then analyzed in adaptive, functional terms.

Examples of such behavior include intention movements, threats, courtship patterns, appeasement gestures, warning calls, distress calls, territorial behavior, overt aggression and maternal behavior. The formation of social bonds, especially in birds, has been shown to depend on exposure to appropriate stimulus objects during a critical period of development (imprinting), and analogies to the formation of social bonds at other times and in other forms have been attempted.

In addition, this approach has resulted in a conceptualization of neurophysiological mechanisms underlying the behaviors. The persuasive writings of Lorenz[6] and Tinbergen[7] have attempted to reason from these animal behavior studies to a more general framework, extending these interpretations of behavior to all species, including our own. The findings and context of ethology, especially where aggressive behavior is concerned, have become well known.[8, 9]

While these approaches have been interesting, persuasive and useful, advances in behavioral genetics and in developmental neurophysiology have given us new tools for arriving at an understanding of the biological basis for behavior as well as for the possibility of predicting and controlling it. A knowledge of neurochemistry, neurophysiology, ultrastructure and the relationship of neural pathways and neural circuity to behavior, and new methods for the investigation of these phenomena, are now at a stage of sophistication where the nervous system can be studied with regard to behavioral states.

Genetic methods and capabilities are also at the stage where it is possible to ask the "nature-nurture" question sensibly and to arrive at meaningful conclusions.

Before reviewing some of the evidence concerning the problem of the genesis and modification of aggressive behavior, a number of methodological points should be clarified to provide the conceptual framework and context for what is to follow. Perhaps the most fundamental point is that the geneticist does not deal with species' specific behavior as the ethologist views it, but rather with the range of individual differences that characterizes a population with respect to any particular effect.

The central tendency of a population produces a picture that complicates analysis in two respects: 1) those individual differences in which we may be particularly interested in any given instance are homogenized and 2) any specific point on a statistical distribution may be arrived at in a *variety* of ways, biologically speaking.

In genetic terminology, this represents a confounding of genotype, phenotype and phenocopy where behavior is concerned. For example, the same behavioral syndrome may arise from a variety of causes. Thus, we may have more than one genetic way of creating the same behavioral predisposition and each might work through somewhat different underlying mechanisms. A so-called phenocopy of a behavioral aberration that can arise from genetic causes may also arise in genetically normal individuals as a result of environmental effects.

As far as any analyses of behavior are concerned, we would, in addition to such phenocopies, expect to find numerous different genetic ways of getting to the same behavioral end result. Each of these will be associated with differences in underlying mechanisms.[10, 11]

When we study the range of behavioral characteristics within a species, we must recognize that each such characteristic may rest on a multiplicity of causal bases, and that a correlation of the behavior under study with any given variable (such as the level of a neural transmitter, a hormonal response, or a change in genic materials) may or may not hold for other instances of what appears to be the identical behavior. Attempts to repeat such correlational (and presumably causal) findings with other samples within the species that may involve a somewhat different genetic sampling may be entirely unsuccessful.[2]

A similar situation obtains on the response side. A pharmacological agent or a manipulative technique that produces a given alteration in behavior in many instances may not work in all.[12] This applies even to brain lesions, where it has recently been shown that the identical lesion in a diverse series of genotypes in the mouse will produce *different* behavioral results, depending on the genetic constitution of the particular mouse.[13]

The method in use in our laboratory involves the simplification of these complicated situations to a point that makes meaningful analysis possible. To achieve this, we have worked with highly inbred strains of mice in which every individual is virtually an identical twin. In this way, we can duplicate a given situation over and over again and compare differences between strains, knowing that we can rely on a certain biological constancy in the genetic substratum.

Our method, then, is to simplify the biological situation as much as we can, depending on the species involved and the material obtainable, and then to do the usual types of studies on a series of individuals, each representing an analyzable genetic background.

With respect to aggression, there is no doubt that the behavior has a heritable basis. Some of the experiments supporting this view have produced some rather amazing results.

My own first experience with heritable aggression occurred as a graduate student working in the laboratory of Professor Sewall Wright on the genetics of guinea pig coat color. Ordinarily, there were no heroics involved in reaching into a cage and removing a guinea pig. Every once in a while, however, this proved to be a blood letting experience. Pedigree analyses showed that the biters traced back to a particular family, and when these were eliminated from the colony, there were no further problems of this sort.

Dr. Paul Sawin, at the Jackson Laboratory, has produced a genetically aggressive stock of rabbits. These arose in a partly inbred line, and selective breeding maintains and intensifies the aggressiveness. In the history of production of dog breeds, selective breeding by amateurs paying attention to behavioral characteristics produced, along with other types of results, an intensification of aggressiveness in some breeds.

The fact that "rough and ready" tests reveal great differences between individuals in a species with respect to aggressive behavior, and that selective breeding can alter the frequency and intensity of such behavior, provides evidence that genetic factors are involved.

In some species, mice, for example, the aggressiveness is seldom encountered in females but is regularly observed in males. In other species, of which wolves are a good example, the females tend to be aggressive toward each other and form their own dominance hierarchy within a pack. It is a familiar observation that in a variety of mammalian species one encounters maternal aggressiveness which can be correlated with hormonal states.

There are many studies implicating male hormone in aggressive behavior. An early one by Beeman provides typical findings, namely that male mice castrated before they have had any fighting experience, generally do not become aggressive.[14] However, they may fight in spite of castration, if aggressive behavior has been allowed to develop. Although this behavior abates after gonadectomy, injection of male hormone will restore it.

Our group has been involved in a number of studies in which, despite very good genetic controls, conflicting results were nevertheless obtained. Thus working with the one strain of mice, we found that under a given condition of rearing, males placed together after sexual maturity were highly combative.[15] Scott, on the other hand, found this same strain of mouse to be the least combative among a number of other strains tested.[16]

In a recent reinvestigation of this problem, using a three-strain comparison, we found the strain in question to be either more highly combative or more pacific, depending on how they were handled during early development.[3] The comparison strains were not affected by the same manipulations, an important point to keep in mind. While these experiments demonstrate that the environmental history is what predisposes these animals, who share a common genotype, toward aggression, a comparison of other genotypes indicates that the same environmental manipulations do not necessarily produce similar results where other strains are concerned.

In the Denenberg et al experiments, the life histories were programmed by rearing mice either on their own mothers *or* on rat mothers.[1] Aggressive behavior occurred among males after sexual maturity in the first instance but not in the second. Denenberg's further findings were that this was not due to nutritional but rather to manipulative factors, especially the retrieving behavior of the mother. These studies provide a close analogue to our own experiments in which the manipulations were performed by the experimenter, and the animal became either aggressive or pacific depending upon the type of manipulation performed relative to the genotype.

In another series of experiments that we have reported comparing different strains, it was found that a variety of manipulations such as cooling, handling, shaking and shocking also had strain specific effects. Stimulation that was effective in altering behavior in one strain did not produce any effect whatsoever in another and affected a third in an opposite direction from the first. The time during the pre-weaning period at which an effect could most readily be produced also varied according to strain. Since each of these situations can be biologically replicated, it is feasible to study the processes involved in these differential responses that are as much determined by the genotype as by the environment.[4]

In another study in our laboratory, in which the variables were manipulated on three different pre-weaning schedules in six strains of mice, and aggressiveness as measured by actual fights among naive mature males was among the measures taken, Jumonville[17] obtained the following results:

Some of the animals were "handled" by placing them individually into a watch glass away from the mother for two minutes each day. Of those so treated, one group was handled daily during the entire preweaning period, another only during the first two weeks of life (days 2-14), and a third during the third and fourth weeks (days 15-27).

In three of the strains tested, the handling significantly affected the fighting behavior. This procedure produced *shorter latencies* to aggression and a *greater number of fights* in two strains of mice. In both instances, the most significant effect was produced by a handling schedule that was carried out during the entire period (days 2-27). In a third strain, a *reduction* in aggression occurred as a result of the handling.

Jumonville also compared two strains, which normally differ in aggression, as well as F_1 animals from reciprocal crosses of these two strains under various conditions of mothering. In only one cross was there a significant effect that could be attributed to the foster mother. The offspring of this cross were less aggressive when raised by mothers from one strain than when raised by mothers from the other strain.

On the basis of evidence of this sort, as well as those obtained from genetic sampling and selection experiments, it has been amply demonstrated that the tendency to fight in a variety of standardized test situations, as well as on more "rough and ready" measures, is heritable. It has also been demonstrated that various pedigrees within a species are highly variable, one from the other, with respect to combativeness.

However, whether a given genotype will be aggressive as an adult or not, can, in many instances, be determined by suitably programming its life history. The timing and the kind of stimulation that is most effective in producing such a change, in a given instance, varies with the genotype.

An attempt to apply these results to other species without elaborate breeding experiments, and to make predictions regarding which individuals will react in which way, would depend upon finding homologies of the underlying mechanisms involved. In this way, one species could serve as the biological model for others, including our own.

What are the mechanisms that we conceive of as being involved in these behaviors? That is to say, how is experience mediated in a neurophysiological and neurochemical way, and what kinds of measurable changes occur in the nervous system when the potential for aggression is changed? Can we manipulate the behavior *regardless of experience* by manipulating the mechanisms, assuming we can identify them? Are we less bound to these mechanisms as we rise in the phylogenetic scale?

Is a mouse, for example, at the mercy of physiological changes, which a man might over-ride through conscious control and training? Assuming that the latter could be demonstrated in some instances, are there others where the genetic instructions are so strong as to structure the behavior completely? These questions have social and legal import, as well as theoretical and therapeutic implications.

As an example, consider the fact that males with an extra Y chromosome, a biological rarity, are, according to some studies, biologically predisposed to violent behavior. This has been introduced into the case of the multiple murderer, Speck, in Illinois, and has also constituted the basis of an acquittal of a murder charge in Australia on grounds of insanity.

According to newspaper accounts of the proceedings, the Melbourne Criminal Court Jury ruled that the defendant was legally insane on the basis of testimony from Dr. Alan Bartholomew, the prison psychiatrist for the

Victorial State Government, who based his contention on the presence of the extra Y. Bartholomew is serving as a member of a panel that has thus far tested 34 prisoners in a Melbourne prison, and found that four had the extra Y chromosome. Of these, two had been convicted of murder and one of attempted murder.

Obviously, the relationship between the extra Y chromosome, central neural processes, and behavior would be difficult to establish in a human subject. Searches for animal models are being carried out. One has been described for the killifish.[18] Suppose we are successful in unraveling the relationship among the extra Y, developmental neural processes, experience and aggressive behavior? The question still remains, that no matter to what degree an abnormality stands in a one-to-one relationship to the behavior in a fish or a rabbit, might there not be a greater effect of will and experience in man, especially if the anomaly is detected early and compensatory training imposed?

There always will be these qualitative differences between man and other species, no matter how closely we can establish the homologies. Only experience with man, based on thorough knowledge obtained from homologies in animal models, will permit us to answer these questions. A recent study by Razavi illustrates both the wealth of materials available, and some of the complications involved.[19]

The work of our own laboratory, using animal models, differs from most other approaches in that it utilizes a developmental genetic approach to behavior.

The developmental approach is one we share with other groups, who have also found that the effect of a lesion in the same area produced at different stages of development may be very different later on. The second, that of the differential effect of the same lesion in different genotypes of the same species, finds its analogy in clinical idiosyncrasies that occur after neuro-surgery. However, in such cases the pedigree data and controls are usually missing.

To return to the specific instance of Maxson's work,[13] we had previously found that a particular gene mutation is associated with an enzyme difference in a specific area of brain.[20, 3] Animals possessing this mutation may convulse upon exposure to a loud noise at weaning age and show a reduced aggression over their controls in later life. However, the possession of the requisite gene will not, by itself, guarantee the behavior. It requires a second, independent mutation to ensure that these behavioral events will transpire.

In his study of this problem, Maxson was able to demonstrate that the lesions would affect the behavior in the combined genotype, but not in the animals that had only the first of the two mutations. In this way, the lesion mimics the missing mutant, while it also demonstrates that the correlation between the genetic anomaly, the altered function and the behavior is very likely causal.

According to the work of Harris,[21] Levine[22] and others, the early handling effects on aggression are very likely mediated by changes in adrenal steroids which, at particular stages of development, organize the brain so that later behavior is altered. This concept was derived by analogy from the work of Young et al with the effects of androgen administered at a sensitive period in development on later sexual behavior.[23]

The times at which some of our effects may be produced (later rather than early during the pre-weaning period for some genotypes, and cumulative across the entire pre-weaning period for others), do not correspond with the period at which the steroid changes affecting later behavior have been reported. It is possible that the same mechanisms are at work but that they are displaced in time or spread across longer time spans in particular strains or stocks. This phenomenon is under investigation. Denenberg and Zarrow recently have provided a re-evaluation of the possible role of hormones and experience in aggression.[24]

Strain differences in serotonin and nor-epinephrine levels, using our stocks of mice do not, so far, correlate in any simple way with the differences we find in aggressive behavior. It could, of course, be that those changes that are the controlling ones occur at the time just prior to the aggressive act, and that the potential for responding at these times is what should be measured. If the genotypes that vary in their aggressive behavior on various experience regimes are indeed affected in this way, we will know it. Generalizations made across genotypes represent so complicated a mix of diverse biological situations, that they are not grist for our mill.

How then do we conceive of these genotype-environment interactions as taking place at the neurophysiological level? A possible model emerging from the researches of our laboratory suggests that biochemical variables associated temporally with the development of the behavior differences in well defined genotypes, are affected by *both* genes and experience. One of the mutants mentioned above as being associated with a localized brain enzyme difference is also the most aggressive genotype of mouse we have (males only).

By stimulating, lesioning and recording from the area in question in the affected and normal genotypes, it should be possible to determine whether this particular localized biochemical change is, indeed, a causal factor in the unusually aggressive behavior of this genotype. If this turns out to be true, why are the males affected differently than the females? Is it a matter of male hormone acting at a particular time in development to change the biochemical capacity of this part of the brain, whereas female hormone will not (or perhaps vice-versa)?

These and other alternatives can now be investigated using a controlled biological substratum. Whether changes in experience that produce changes in aggression work through these same mechanisms can also be investigated in the same way. The pioneering work of Delgado has provided convincing demonstration that stimulation of given brain areas in a behavioral context can both initiate and suppress aggression during various social interactions, thereby modifying social behavior.[25]

These techniques can now be extended in view of the availability of appropriate animal models in order to permit the investigation of individual genetic and experiential differences as these interact during development to produce individuals with basically more and less aggressive dispositions.

With respect to the second mutation mentioned in the context of the lesion experiments, the biochemical effects of the genes on brain biochemistry during development have been described.[26, 27] It has been possible to create phenocopies in normal animals that mimic the effect of the mutant at both the biochemical and behavioral level: (a) By manipulating the auditory input at the 19th day post-partum,[17, 18] or (b) By manipulating the underlying biochemical system using enzyme inhibitors.[26.] In essence, by analyzing how a gene acts to alter a behavioral capacity during development, it becomes possible to intervene at the appropriate time and reproduce this action in an individual who would otherwise not be programmed this way genetically.

In the instance referred to, a permanent change has been effected that endows the individual with the same capacity he would have if he were a genetic mutant. The difference being, of course, that in the case of the mutant, the genetic capacity will be passed on to the offspring, whereas in the case of the phenocopy, it will not. This hypothesis and its supporting data have been more fully described elsewhere.[29, 30]

The essentials of the model are that the genetic capacities, for a variety of behavioral responses, in the form of programmed neural mechanisms, exist in most members of a population, and genes predisposing to a particular type of behavior do so by means of activating and/or suppressing the action of other genes. Since the building blocks for a wide variety of behaviors are present despite these genetic restrictions, biological intervention, either by stimulation or by direct biochemical manipulation of some of the processes involved at the time when one or another gene would normally be activated can *change* the *behavioral predisposition* in a manner *directly analogous* to a genetic mutation.

This hypothesis, derived from the study of several mutants, offers an existing possibility for the better utilization of the range of genetic mechanisms available to an individual, including the possibility of overcoming genetic defects. It is, of course, one thing to be able to do this in a mouse, where the evidence can be obtained and studied so that the sensitive periods and the systems affected are made known, and quite another to attempt it clinically.

However, even the *understanding* of these mechanisms opens up new directions and changes our thinking with respect to how genes act in determining behavioral potentials.

Finally, the methodological considerations represented by these investigations are of paramount importance, since it is not sufficient to have a correlation between a behavioral syndrome and some aspect of neuromorphology and/or neurophysiology, or even to be able to manipulate the behavior in a genetically mixed population by means of drugs,, lesions and programmed experience. Every syndrome can contain a variety of genotypes, each tied to a somewhat different underlying mechanism, as well as a number of phenocopies that have arisen in still other ways.

These must be detected and separately analyzed to achieve any real understanding of the biological basis of any behavior, including the lack of equivalence in behavioral outcome of identical experiences and manipulations when applied to diverse genotypes within the same species. This is an extremely difficult field, and we would do well to simplify and control our variables until our understanding in this area brings us to a threshhold from which a quantum jump in our ability to understand and control behavior can occur.

REFERENCES

1. Denenberg, V. H., Hudgens, G. A., and Zarrow, M. X.: Science 143:380, 1964.
2. Ginsburg, B. E.: Social Serv. Rev. 40:121, 1966.
3. Ginsburg, B. E.: In *Behavior-Genetic Analysis,* pp. 135-153, ed. Hirsch, J., New York: McGraw Hill, 1967.
4. Ginsburg, B. E.: Science and Psychoanalysis, 12:12, 1968.
5. Scott, J. P.: Science, 138:949, 1962.
6. Lorenz, K.: *Evolution and Modification of Behavior,* Chicago, The University of Chicago Press, 1965.
7. Tinbergen, N.: Advan. Sci., 12:17, 1955.
8. Lorenz, K.: *On Aggression,* (Translation of *Das Sogenannte Bose,* Vienna, Borotha-Schoeber, 1963.) M. Wolf, Tr. New York: Harcourt, Brace and World, 1966.
9. Morris, D.: *The Naked Ape,* London, Jonathan Cape, 1967.
10. Ginsburg, B. E.: Perspect. Biol. Med., 1:397, 1958.
11. Ginsburg, B. E.: In *Concepts of Personality,* pp. 63-78, eds. Wepman, J. W. and Heine, R. W., Chicago, Aldine Press, 1963.
12. Ginsburg, B. E.: Proc. Ass. Res. Nerv. Ment. Dis., 33:39, 1954.
13. Maxson, S. C.: Dissertation, Department of Psychology, University of Chicago, 1966.
14. Beeman, E. A.: Physiol. Zool., 20:373, 1947.
15. Ginsburg, B. E. and Allee, W. C.: Physiol. Zool., 15:485, 1942.
16. Scott, J. P.: J. Hered., 33:11, 1942.
17. Jumonville, J. E.: Dissertation, Department of Psychology, University of Chicago, 1968.
18. Hamilton, J. B., Walter, R. O., Daniel, R. M., and Mestler, G. E.: An. Behav., 17:168, 1969.
19. Razavi, L.: A.A.A.S. Symposium: *The Biology and Sociology of Violence,* In press.
20. Cowen, J. S.: Dissertation, Department of Psychology, University of Chicago, 1966.
21. Harris, G. W.: Endocrinology, 75:627, 1966.
22. Levine, S., and Treiman, L. J.: In Foetal Autonomy, pp. 271-281, eds. G. E. W. Wolstenholme and Maeve O'Connor, Ciba Foundation Symposium, London, J. & A. Churchill Ltd., 1969.
23. Young, W. C., Goy, R. W., and Phoenix, C. H.: In *Sex Research, New Developments,* pp. 176-196, ed. Money, J., New York, Holt, Rinehart and Winston, 1965.
24. Denenberg, V. H., and Zarrow, M. X.: Psychol. Today, 3, 45, 1969.
25. Delgado, J. M. R.: Journ. Nerv. Ment. Dis., 144:383, 1967.
26. Sze, P.: In A.A.A.S. Symposium on *Physiological Effects of Audible Sound (Extra-Auditory),* ed., Welch, B. L. In press. 1970.
27. Ginsburg, B. E., Cowen, J. S., Maxson, S. C., and Sze, P.: Progress in Neuro-Genetics, 1:695, 1970.
28. Henry, K. R.: Science, 158:938, 1967.
29. Ginsburg, B. E.: In *Foetal Autonomy,* pp. 286-299, eds. G. E. W. Wolstenholme and

Maeve O'Connor, Ciba Foundation Symposium, London, J. & A. Churchill Ltd., 1969.
30. Ginsburg, B. E.: In *Stimulation in Early Infancy*, pp. 73-97, ed., Ambrose, A., London, New York: Academic Press, 1969.

COPING WITH AGGRESSION AMONG NORMAL ADOLESCENT BOYS*

Daniel Offer, M.D.

Introduction

Do all adolescents have difficulties with their aggressive feelings? Are these aggressive feelings uniformly so intense as to make the ego of the teenager helpless in the presence of mounting tension? If a significant number of teenagers are able to curb their aggression, and release their frustration in socially acceptable ways, how do they do it? Does the successful coping of certain teenagers help us understand why others are not able to curb their aggression? If one of the most important and difficult tasks of the adolescent is to learn how to release his aggression in a non-destructive way, why do so many obviously fail in their task?

In order to attempt to answer these difficult questions I report our experience and findings from a longitudinal study of normal adolescents over the past seven years.

Selecting the Normal Adolescents

In the book *Normality*,[1] Sabshin and I discussed the problem of selection of normal subjects. We based our selection on a statistical approach, *normality as average,* which is useful for group research and which we hoped would help eliminate extremes of psychopathology or superior adjustment. We wanted to select a modal group from the widest possible spectrum of teenagers living in a particular community. A natural choice was a high school

*Supported by Public Health Service Research Grants M-4870 and MH 08814 from the National Institute of Mental Health and 02571 from the National Institute for Child Health and Human Development.

Dr. Offer is associate director of the Institute for Psychosomatic and Psychiatric Research and Training at Michael Reese Hospital and Medical Center, and associate professor of psychiatry at Pritzker School of Medicine, University of Chicago, Chicago, Illinois.

attended by all teenagers in one community. We believed that two different high schools representing the range of the middle class would assure a better sample than, for example, twice as large a group in one high school. It would also avoid findings biased by the selection of a special school.

In the Fall of 1962, a self-image questionnaire was given to 326 freshmen boys in the two suburban high schools. Of the original 103 students who met the statistical and behavioral criteria, 73 subjects have remained active in all aspects of the project throughout the high school years.

We believe that we succeeded in selecting adolescent subjects who are significantly different psychologically from disturbed adolescents seen in psychiatric practice. Only seven of the 103 students, or about 7 per cent, had moderately severe emotional problems which became manifest in the course of our longitudinal contact with them.

Our subjects were studied in the following way:
1. Each subject was interviewed eight times during the high school years, and once yearly for the next three years.
2. Each subject had a complete battery of psychological testing (Rorschach, TAT and Whecsler Verbal IQ), during the junior year.
3. Parents of all subjects were interviewed to obtain additional information about the subjects.
4. The boys' school records were available to us. They included the extensive grading of behavior by teachers in the high schools.[2]

Results

When we first interviewed our high school subjects, they were in their freshman year. The majority said that their most difficult problem was how to act in a socially acceptable way. They told us that they often had strong urges to give vent to their negative, rebellious or aggressive impulses. Very few of our subjects acted in violent or destructive ways; but almost all of them acted in a manner which we defined as rebellious: open resistance to, or defiance of, any authority.[3]

The rebellion had manifested itself most clearly in early adolescence, at ages 12 and 13. The boys described themselves as "getting into fights with our parents," for seemingly small and insignificant issues. For example, they broke the rules of the house by refusing to take the garbage out, dressing differently, coming home late, not making their beds, or going out with "the wrong crowd." They did not go to church as often as their parents did. Rebellious behavior carried over to school teachers, church workers, and other significant adult males.

The rebellion was characterized by chronic in-fighting for one to two years with parents and school teachers over issues which seem small or non-dramatic. There usually were no great pitched battles over crucial or world-shaking issues. We want to emphasize that this miniature guerrilla warfare had vital and important meaning to the adolescent in this stage of his development. The parents of these adolescents did not regard their sons' behavior as trivial. The overwhelming majority of the parents said that the early adolescent years (12 to 14) were the most difficult times that they had in raising their children.

Our adolescent subjects did show a certain degree of conformity to each other in behavior, values, dress, recreation and consumer consumption. But, this conformity did not make them any less rebellious at home. Based on our definition of rebellion the object of rebellious behavior is the authority figure, and conforming, ritualistic behavior in groups of boys their own age did not rule out defiance to parents.

Our observations have been that adolescents can and do rebel while still conforming to their parents' system of values; i.e., the teenagers maintained the same middle-class values as their parents had. They had the same class biases, claimed allegience to the same religious denominations as their parents and intended to pursue their fathers' occupations, either the same or class-related ones.

According to Erikson,[4] a psychosocial moratorium is provided by each society to allow a period of time for the adolescent to experiment, play around, and test before he commits himself to a certain role. The high school environment can serve as one example where the adolescent is free to try his wings, and where society, the family and school are willing to give him time by permitting open rebellious behavior within certain limits, and, as it were, not letting it count.

In our study, individual rebellion in high school ceased to a great extent, and took on a more systematized and institutionalized form.

For example, in the two high schools 50 per cent of the students were active smokers, at any one time. Because of their habit, they, just as the teachers who smoked, wanted to smoke during lunch hours. But, in contrast to the teachers, the students did not have a lounge where smoking was permitted.

Therefore, they developed an arrangement with the school by which they didn't really defy the rules openly, and yet didn't accept them either. In one of the schools the students would cross the street, stand within half a block of the school and smoke during their lunch hour. In the other school, many students would smoke in the bathroom while one of their peers watched for the teacher, who was "on patrol" that particular day. When the teacher came near the bathroom, the look-out would whistle a particular tune and the cigarettes would be flushed down the toilet. When the teacher went into the washroom, which was, of course, full of smoke, he could not catch any of the students smoking. He then simply asked all of them to leave the washroom. This was repeated several times each day.

Often such accommodations are passed down to the next younger generation of adolescents and a tradition develops. The adolescents' rebellion and the school's method of coping with it will then become ritualized and institutionalized for succeeding generations of adolescents. As we can see from the above example this was not only an institutionalized form of rebellion, but it gave the teachers and parents (i.e., "the authorities") something to smile about.

Our subjects varied in the extent of their rebellious behavior. In some, whose ability to control impulses was less developed, we did see some violent behavior. We can illustrate our subjects' ways of handling aggression by the example of Lester.

Lester was 13 years old when his parents moved to a suburb from the big city. He was a short stocky boy, eager to please the interviewer and proud of his athletic achievements. One major reason for the move was to allow Lester to benefit from the better school system in the suburbs.

Lester did not see the move in a similar perspective. He was now far away from his friends and was not yet part of the group in his new environment. He missed his old friends and would go back to the old neighborhood (which was far away, almost an hour by public transportation) whenever he could. His performance in school was poorer than before, and, although he was passing all his subjects, his parents were concerned with his academic standing. When his parents learned about his trips to the old neighborhood they strictly forbade them. Nonetheless, Lester, who was now 14, continued to go.

A few months later he was in a serious physical fight with another member of the old clique who made fun of his small size. The fight led to a serious, though not chronic, injury to the other boy (fracture of a bone), and the fight had to be broken up by the police. The police told Lester that they would not inform his parents of the incident if there were no recurrence and he would "stay out of trouble." The parents were not aware of this particular incident. Lester learned from his experience and was motivated to drop his old friends and develop more appropriate friendships in his new environment. For Lester the rebellion was over.

Lester was given psychological tests at age 16, approximately two years after this incident. At the time Lester took the tests he appeared to be a youngster who was very concerned about what he did that was wrong. He virtually divided his actions into good and evil. Despite considerable pressure to be a good boy and to stop doing bad things, the tests showed he was preoccupied with hostile and destructive feelings.

There seemed to be some anxiety connected with being good, as though being good prevented him from easily discriminating himself from his father. There was also the feeling that he would not be doing bad things for very long, that basically he was a good person, and that things would turn out well.

There was resentment toward his father as an intruder, but a very strong pull to take from him and be like him. He ambivalently tried to hurt his father, to rub salt in his wounds, but then felt not only guilty, but also anxious that this would push his father completely away from him. He looked toward his mother as a control, but felt that he had a lesser need for her because he should now be able to use his own resources.

He was an introspective youngster, who kept his feelings for the most part to himself. There was little opportunity for release of feelings or for confirming how he saw reality. He was quite reactive to affective stimulation, but could allow himself no satisfactory outlet. So, he was a rather uncomfortable youngster, but one whose concentration and resourcefulness allowed him to function productively.

The case of Lester has been presented to illustrate how one particular teenager coped with his aggressive impulses. In early adolescence, Lester was not only rebellious; he was also violent. But he quickly learned that there were appropriate ways to channel his aggression. Though at 16 he still struggled with his aggression, he now demonstrated to himself and others that he could cope with these feelings and impulses on his own. In other words, Lester began to develop inner controls which were aiding him in mastering his own aggression.

Lester demonstrated both rebellious and violent or delinquent behavior. The relationship between juvenile delinquency and adolescent rebellion is an important one. Although the two forms of behavior share attributes in common, rebellion is not delinquency. Rebellious acts which remain within the confines of the home and are acts of defiance clearly and solely against the rules of the home should not be confused with delinquency. Only when rebellious acts involve the law and ethics of society at large can they be said to be delinquent.

In our sample, 25 per cent of our subjects said they had participated in at least one delinquent act as defined above. Fifty-two per cent of our subjects told us that they had known or associated closely with persons who had been involved in delinquent acts. The delinquent acts of our subjects consisted of stealing—money and goods from stores, and, on rare occasions, cars—throwing coke bottles on major highways, vandalism and serious physical fights. Other, milder acts included overturning dozens of garbage cans after a football game.

As we stressed in the case of Lester, the vast majority of our subjects who did participate in delinquent acts ceased this particular form of behavior after one or two trials. Only 3 per cent of our sample have had chronic difficulties controlling their impulses.

We followed 60 of the 73 subjects for the first three post high school years. The main finding concerning aggression was that the previous outlets were no longer available to them. A large number were now mildly depressed. The depression had a diffuse quality.

For example, John appreciated the qualities of his university, but did not like the community. "It is hard to live in a ghetto where you can't go out at night. Everything is gloomy. It is just the environment." Of course, he added with a smile, "maybe it is also me."

Throughout the rest of the interview, John, who was doing very good work, was berating himself and his ability. He also was unhappy because he had no close friends and dated infrequently. Despite the above, his plans for the future were definite.

Discussion

Aggression is defined by Lorenz[5] as that "fighting instinct in beast and man which is directed against members of the same species." Its universial presence in man also was described by Freud[6] who believed that the destructive (or death) instinct is "at work in every living being and is striving to bring it to ruin and to reduce life to its original condition of inanimate matter." Similarly, Tinbergen[7] states that "the elimination through education of the internal urge to fight will turn out to be very difficult, if not impossible to achieve."

The question which must concern us, therefore, is not whether we can eliminate aggression and violence, but rather how we as humans can learn to cope with our aggressive impulses. The learning process must begin early in childhood as the child is taught *how to tolerate frustration and to accept delay of gratification.* This "goal directed behavior"[8] is essentially learned first in the home and then in the school.

The child who has not been taught to tolerate frustration in the home environment will find it exceedingly difficult to curb his aggression once he reaches adolescence. His increased strength as an adolescent will make him potentially more dangerous to society. During puberty these aggressive feelings become more intense as the child grows in physical stature, experiences intense sexual feelings, and begins to separate from his parents.

The two main pathogenic methods of upbringing—over-strictness and over-indulgence—have been accurately assessed by Hartmann.[9] Hartmann states that the "unduly lenient and indulgent father" is the cause of children forming an overly strict super-ego, because their impression of paternal love leaves them no outlet for their aggressiveness other than turning it inwards. In delinquent children, who have been brought up without love, the tension between ego and super-ego is lacking, and the whole of their aggressiveness can be directed outwards.

Our subjects coped with aggression in the following ways. During the formative years (up to high school) they were taught to channel their aggression in socially, or familially, acceptable ways. They learned to tolerate frustration and internalized their parents' standards and values. They felt very much part of the smaller (familial) and larger (societal) environments. It was, therefore, not only a matter of obeying an external authority out of fear, but also a true internalization of standards.[10]

The subjects had some difficulties controlling their aggressive feelings and impulses in early adolescence. There were some violent outbursts and delinquent behavior. In high school, the aggressive impulse was sublimated most often into competitive sports. This sublimation was supported by the students' total milieu, from teachers and parents to peers. Open aggression in athletics in the high school setting was fostered. The students used sports more than intellectual pursuits as their route for aggressive discharge. Yet they participated in our project which demanded a kind of behavior that was passive by nature (i.e., talking as contrasted with doing).

The gratification which they received was twofold. First, they had the opportunity to talk with an "objective" adult. Second, they did obtain intellectual satisfaction from participating in this project. They expanded their knowledge about themselves and learned more about other teenagers.

After high school most of the subjects learned to channel their aggression into studying, work, or sexual activities. We saw mild depressive feelings in our subjects after high school because the method of handling aggression was not yet completely effective. On these occasions the aggression was turned inward; hence, the depression.

The controlled utilization of anger and hostility was yet another way the students sublimated their aggressive feelings and impulses. It might have included participation in the debating team, or, in a more mundane way, a "good fight" with a sibling, who almost always served as a handy target.

Humor was frequently used by our subjects as a way of expressing hostility. Much tension was released once the joke was told, and the underlying hostility was understood and expressed; no overt harm was done. Our adolescents' use of humor as an expression of hostility was not always as obvious as in the oft-told story of Heine[11] who said:

Mine is a most peaceful disposition. My wishes are: a humble cottage with a thatched roof, but a good bed, good food, the freshest milk and butter, flowers before my window, and a few fine trees before my door; and if God wants to make my happiness complete, he will grant me the joy of seeing some six or seven of my enemies hanging from these trees.

Obviously there are many factors which enter into an individual's ability to curb his aggression. It seems appropriate to close this presentation with the following statement of Freud: "The *postponement of gratification* (is) an important element in the process of sublimation and thereby essential to (normal) development."[12]

Conclusion

We have presented data from a specially selected group of 73 normal adolescent boys who have been studied for the past seven years. We have shown what kinds of problems they had with their aggressive feelings and impulses and how they coped with them.

REFERENCES

1. Offer, D. and Sabshin, M.: *Normality,* Basic Books, Inc., New York, 1966.
2. Offer, D.: *The Psychological World of the Teen-Ager,* Basic Books, Inc., New York, 1969.
3. Baittle, B. and Offer, D.: *On the Nature of Adolescent Rebellion,* Annals of Adolescent Psychiatry, S. Feinstein, P. Giovacchine and A. Miller (eds.) Basic Books, Inc., New York (In Press).
4. Erikson, E.: *Identity: Youth and Crisis,* W. W. Norton & Company, New York, 1968.
5. Lorenz, K.: *On Aggression,* Bantam Book, New York, 1966.
6. Freud, S.: Collected Papers, Ed. J. Stachey, Vol. 5, Basic Books, Inc., New York, 1961.
7. Tinbergen, N.: Science 160:1411, 1968.
8. Herrick, C. J.: *The Evolution of Human Nature,* University of Texas Press, Austin, 1956.
9. Hartmann, H.: Psychoanal Stud Child, Vol. 8, 1953.

10. Beres, D.: Psychoanalytic Considerations, P5a, Q.XXXVII; 4, 487, 1968.

11. Heine, H.: *Gedanken und Einfalle*, Section I in Sämtliche Werke, Vol. 4, Leipzig, 1887.

12. Freud, S.: as quoted by Helena Deutsch in *Selected Problems of Adolescence*, International Universities Press, New York, 1967.

ADOLESCENT AGGRESSION AND DEPENDENCE

**Edward J. Rolde, M.D. and
George W. Goethals, Ed.D.**

Present interest in aggression of adolescents is part of the growing concern over violence and aggression in modern society. It is probably easier to document an increased *fear* of violence than it is to document an increased *amount* of violence. Much of this increased fear seems to relate to increased destructiveness. The atom bomb is obviously a more fearful weapon than the bow and arrow.

With increased power to destroy, and an increased fear of aggression, there is an increased ability and likelihood of retaliation against those we fear. It is significant that much of our concern with aggression is being channeled toward the young. The term "adolescent aggression" has become an epithet in the present idiom, much as the term "damyankee" in the old South. As we become increasingly concerned and skilled in dealing with adolescent aggression, we should be sensitive to the effects which our efforts have on the adolescent.

There is much in the current literature to suggest that we have a good deal about which to be sensitive. A principal concern, for example, of many of the documents of the recent President's Task Force on Delinquency[1] is what is being done *to* the adolescent in the name of what is being done *for* him.

Another example is the point made by Chein in the *Road to H*[2], where he raises the possibility that the public attitude towards strict suppression of drug abuse is one of the factors that contribute to increased abuse.

There is a serious danger in the increasing tendency of adult society to view large segments of adolescent behavior as "aggression." The tendency to see "aggression" everywhere is supported by the lack of agreement in current theory as to what constitutes (the meaning of) aggression. A perusal of

---

Dr. Rolde is Director of Legal Medicine at Massachusetts Mental Health Center, Boston, and instructor in psychiatry at Harvard; Dr. Goethals is lecturer on social relations, Harvard.

the literature will uncover many discussions of aggression, but few explications of what is meant by the term. Much behavior that is seen within a framework of aggression could be better understood and dealt with if it were seen within the framework of dependency.

One basic problem is the difficulty in distinguishing between the objective consequences of an action and the motivation behind it. The objective consequences are the more visible and easily measured; the motivation is more often inferred from them. It is especially easy for an observer who feels threatened by the consequences of an action to believe that the motivation for the action is an aggressive one.

In the classic literary situation, the young man announces his presence by tossing a stone up against the young lady's window. From the lady's point of view, the observable fact is the stone striking the window; the unknown is the subjective disposition of the shadowy figure in the dark below. If, in an anxious mood, she regards the stone striking the window as an attack, she is likely to respond differently than if she feels the purpose is to attract her attention. The old adage, "shoot first, ask questions later" can be useful in some situations, dangerous in many others.

Retaliatory action may be most inappropriate when behavior that is motivated by a need for dependence is looked up as aggressive. The crying of an infant often has been cited in the literature as an example of aggressive behavior. Probably all mothers find their baby's crying irritating some of the time. If the mother experiences the crying as an attack, her actions are likely to be less appropriate than if she experiences it as a communication of hunger or need. How the crying is experienced may depend principally on the projective system of the mother. When the baby's crying is seen as an attack, the results can be disastrous for both mother and child.

In our social system, individuals can feel under personal attack from actions they perceive as threats to the society of which they are a part. An example is the deep personal involvement and fear on the part of large numbers of Americans concerning what they think is the constant Communist menace.

There are several types of behavior that can appear threatening to a society. Aggression is one. No society can exist very long with an unlimited amount of aggression among its members. But it is also true that no self-sufficient society can survive if all its members refuse to take responsibility for themselves. In economic terms, a society cannot exist if none of its members produces anything.

The assignment and maintenance of role-status relationships is another prerequisite for social survival. To function in a society, individuals must have a general schema of what to expect from others and what is expected of them. By threatening the existence of society itself, individuals who exhibit excessively violent behavior, and also those who exhibit excessively dependent behavior or who refuse to identify themselves with the role structure of the society, can appear as personal threats to members of that society.

Whether it was true of other times, it is a phenomenon of ours that adult society feels threatened by the very existence of adolescents. The adolescent is in a state of suspension, manifestly ready to assume adult roles, but not having assumed them yet. He is a very threatening individual: threatening society by his delay in assuming adult roles, and, at the same time, threatening to compete with adults by displacing them in their roles. It is obvious that adolescents can be aggressive. It is an age group or social grouping with much to be aggressive about for many reasons.

However, the fact that adolescents can be aggressive does not justify classifying all adolescent behavior as such. Much that we do classify as aggressive is behavior that reflects a failure of the adolescent to take responsibility as the adult society thinks he should.

We will present three varied instances of the current misuse of the "adolescent aggression" label. Wolfgang voices the sentiment of American criminology when he says: "The public image of a vicious, violent juvenile population producing a seemingly steady increase in violent crimes is not substantiated by the evidence available."[3] This statement can be taken as a comment on the public image of juveniles as much as it can be taken as a comment on juvenile crime.

The terms "juvenile delinquency" and "adolescent aggression" or "violence" are being used interchangeably with increasing frequency despite the fact that the incidence of violence against persons remains quite a small proportion of total juvenile offenses. The largest grouping of offenses[4], (e.g., runaway, stubborn child, truancy from school), consists of charges more related to issues of responsibility than to issues of aggression. The other major grouping (e.g., theft, automobile theft and joy riding, narcotics, etc.) can perhaps best be interpreted in terms of adolescents trying to have a good time, or at least trying to obtain the means with which to do so.

We do not mean to deny that aggression can be expressed indirectly; stealing clearly can be involved in a boy's hostility toward his parents or society. However, the concept of indirect aggression is of doubtful value if it results in classifying all adolescent behavior as aggressive. The view that all or most adolescents being brought before the courts are violent or aggressive distorts the facts.

The scholarly literature, as well as public sentiment, shows questionable use of the label "aggressive." The study *Adolescent Aggression* by Bandura and Walters[5] is one of the most respected and influential in the field, especially for those with a behavioristic leaning. This study compared 26 aggressive boys with 26 controls. Also interviewed were their families, with a focus on child-rearing practices.

Nowhere in the study is there any explicit, formal, theoretical or operational explanation of what the authors mean by the word "aggression." There is no detailed description of what the aggressive boys did to get themselves classified as aggressive; there is no discussion of the possibility that there might be some theoretical or operational difficulty in deciding which adolescents should be labeled aggressive. There is an implication that the terms aggressive and antisocial are considered synonyms. The words often are used together as a single term.

It seems that the boys were chosen because they were in trouble with the law, and/or because they were described as antisocial by school authorities, probation officers and guidance workers. It is stated that the relevant behavior for the inclusion of at least some of the boys was truancy. It appears likely that the behavior of every boy chosen did get some one angry at him, and that this anger on the part of those in authority might have been the common denominator for inclusion in the aggressive category.

A major conclusion of the study was that the child-rearing practices of the parents of the aggressive boys were characterized more by the way that they handled issues of dependence than by the way they handled issues of aggression. It seems highly possible that what is presented in the literature as the psychological development of a group of aggressive boys could more properly be presented as the psychological development of a group of dependent boys.

As a further clinical example of the effects of the questionable use of the aggressive label, we would like to discuss briefly the case of a 19-year-old boy recently presented for parole consideration at the maximum security institution for juveniles in one of the eastern states. The boy demonstrates a too common occurrence: a late adolescent, having spent most of his adolescent years in institutions as a danger to society, but with only a minor record of delinquent behavior, a record characteristically composed largely of truancy and running away.

The boy had been termed the "future Albert DeSalvo" in one of the psychiatric reports written during his institutional career. (Albert DeSalvo is the man publicized as the Boston Strangler, perpetrator of about 16 brutal murders.)[6] "The future Albert DeSalvo," was repeated in numerous reports in the boy's record.

It is not surprising that shudders ran through any official gathering which had considered his parole, and that it was a good deal easier to find persons willing to take the responsibility for keeping him in an institution than it was to find persons willing to take the responsibility for letting him go.

This boy had been adopted as an infant by a family who subsequently had their own natural children, and thereafter let him know in many ways that he was not wanted. He was first institutionalized at age 12 for repeated truancy, and was released at age 15. He was then reinstitutionalized several months later under a charge of assault. This charge stemmed from an incident that consisted essentially of voyeurism with no allegation of the use of force. His parents agreed on the institutionalization, saying they were afraid that he had shown sexual curiosity with their natural children.

For the next four years his record consisted of several escape attempts. He soon began turning himself in after being successful in leaving the institution; each of his escape attempts was made shortly before a time when he was scheduled for release. On one occasion he had a short unsuccessful placement in the state police barracks. The "future DeSalvo" nickname had come after alleged confessions of sex crimes, all supposedly during times when he was in institutions. It was difficult to tell from the record whose imagination and fantasies had stimulated these stories, the boy's or those of person's who had interviewed him. Psychological testing showed possible minimal brain damage, but no especially aggressive ideation.

When the time for his latest scheduled release arrived, the boy understandably became increasingly anxious. He made an escape attempt, turned himself in, and seemed quite disappointed when it didn't result in a prolonged sentence. Completely disowned by his parents, he was scheduled to take a room in a YMCA in a city in the central part of the state, a city in which he knew no one and which he had never visited.

Questioning showed that he had little idea of how to manage the realities of everyday life on his own. His classification as a highly aggressive individual had meant that the major effort of the youth authority of the state had been spent in keeping him in an institution, away from society. If he had been classified as a dependent individual, it would have become clear that the major problem was to keep him *out* of institutions and to get him to relate to society instead of to institutions. Of course, he had learned from experience that if things got tough, raising the spectre of aggression was a certain way back to the safety of the institution.

The history of this boy is reminiscent of the social breakdown syndrome, a concept that has been developed with regard to chronic schizophrenics.[7] Preoccupied with fear and perhaps hatred of schizophrenics, society found it easier to keep them in institutions than in the community. Many of the symptoms that were long considered to be the chronic symptoms of schizophrenia are now believed to be a product of institutional communication. The chronically institutionalized adolescent, instead of being considered the prototype of the dangerous juvenile, is perhaps closer to the prototype of the institutionalized dependent.

The lack of definition in current theories of aggression is one of the factors that support the increasing amount of behavior labelled as aggressive. The term is used repeatedly with little consensus as to its definition. Tinbergen says "We all understand the term (aggression) in some vague general way, but it is after all no more than a catchword."[8] The most productive question, however, is not what the word means but which problems a theory of aggression is supposed to solve. The most pressing need is for a theory that will help differentiate the types of violent behavior.

The central concern in most present theoretical discussions is the debate about whether aggression is an innate drive or whether it is stimulated by external conditions and circumstances. Behaviorist psychology generally represents the latter view; psychoanalytic psychology considers aggression an innate drive. Theories in both schools imply that aggression is a psychological concept, differing from the strictly behavioral concept of violence. Neither has given much attention to distinguishing behavior having as its goal the pleasure of hurting another person from behavior which aims at attracting attention or gaining material reward. Neither theoretical system has dealt successfully with the problem of differentiating dependent from aggressive behavior.

Most discussions of aggression in the behaviorist category refer back to the monograph by Dollard *et al*, "Frustration and Aggression."[9] The authors stated: "Aggression is independently defined as an act whose goal-response is injury to an organism." Two types of behavior were specifically excluded from the definition: accidental violence, and what was termed "instrumental" aggression—i.e., behavior primarily directed toward some goal other than doing injury.

The task of operationally distinguishing dependent from aggressive behavior is specifically discussed in an influential paper on child-rearing by Sears et al.[10] The authors suggest that, while there is a correlation between aggressive and dependent patterns of behavior, it is important and feasible for future studies to analyze them independently. Subsequent papers in the behaviorist school, however, even by the same authors, do not follow the suggestion.

As has been discussed in relation to the Bandura and Walters study, works in the behaviorist tradition place a wide variety of violent and anti-social acts in the category of aggression. Aggression is operationally defined as any behavior that injures. This is a definition close to the concept of violence. It is inherent in behaviorist psychology that a distinction according to motivation cannot be made easily. Such distinction would imply a cognitive framework and an examination of what is in "the black box," a pursuit not in the tradition of most behaviorists.

The usefulness of psychoanalytic theory also has been limited by lack of explicit definition of aggression. Freud developed his thinking on the subject relatively late,[11] and it remains one of the least well developed concepts of his system.

Again, one of the influential articles in the field can be used as an example: "Notes on the Theory of Aggression" by Hartman, Kris, and Loewenstein.[12] In this article aggression is discussed at length, but nowhere defined. The word aggressive is followed occasionally in a parenthetical expression by the words "manifestations of destructiveness" and sometimes by the word "cruelty." In other words, there is uncertainty as to whether "aggression" is to be used synonymously with the word "violence" or as a concept smiliar to the concept of sadism.

In the psychoanalytically oriented literature Menninger upholds Freud's formulation of the death instinct;[13] Fenichal maintains that aggression arises from the frustration of other drives;[14] Hartman, Kris, and Loewenstein stress the independent nature of the aggressive drive.[12] Given the lack of definition of the term "aggression" in these writings, these differing views can be taken to represent differences of opinions as to what the word means, rather than differing views on the nature of a phenomenon.

The field of biology has been the most fruitful in trying to differentiate the concept of aggression from the concept of violence. This is a necessity if a theory of aggression is going to be used to understand violent behavior. Biological works frequently postulate explicitly the basic question that they are trying to answer.

To quote Tinbergen again, "Why is man, as opposed to other animals, so destructive of each other?"[8] i.e., why so much violence among men? The finding that has generated the most interest is the theory stating that so-called aggressive behavior among other species is most often not designed to hurt, but to communicate or otherwise bloodlessly settle an issue (for example, the control of territory).[15] Some animals have two sets of horns; one for the sham battle and the other for real battles.[16]

Animals go through threatening motions but settle differences without fighting to kill or injure. The circumstance of behavior designed to hurt is not the same as the circumstance of behavior designed to settle an issue. The two types of activity have many similarities but are clearly distinguishable when examined closely. A theoretical framework or terminology that does not differentiate them has limited usefulness.

To summarize: we are witnessing and taking part in an increasing preoccupation with questions of aggression and violence. A major focus of this increased concern is the adolescent. Adolescents are often regarded as aggressive because they threaten the established society. The tendency to view large segments of adolescent behavior as aggressive is a point of view, but only one of several alternatives.

By misapplying the label "aggressive," we run the risk of increasing adolescent aggressive activity by blocking originality and expression normal to this age, and by presupposing the identity of the adolescent aggressor. Many problems of adolescence which are categorized as problems of aggression could be better understood if seen as attempts to resolve ambivalence between dependence and independence.

There is a need for a theory of aggression that will distinguish among the different categories of violence; between violence committed for the pleasure of hurting others and violence committed as a means of communication; or for other specific goals.

Erikson sums up the matter well when he describes adolescence as a period of struggle to form a sense of identity. He states ". . . should a child feel that the environment tries to deprive him too radically of all the forms of expression which permit him to develop and to integrate the next step in his ego identity, he will resist with the astonishing strength encountered in animals who are suddenly forced to defend their lives . . . Yet many a youth, finding that the authorities expect him to be a 'bum' or a 'queer,' or 'off the beam,' perversely obliges by becoming just that."[17]

REFERENCES

1. President's Commission on Law Enforcement and Administration of Justice, *Task Force Report—Juvenile Delinquency and Youth Crime,* U.S. Goverment Printing Office, Washington, 1967.
2. Chein, I., et al: *The Road to II,* Basic Books, New York, 1964.
3. Wolfgang, M. E.: "The Culture of Youth", *Task Force Report—Juvenile Delinquency and Youth Crime,* U.S. Government Printing Office, Washington, 1967.
4. Tappan, P.: *The Nature of Juvenile Delinquency,* McGraw-Hill, New York, 1949.
5. Bandura, A. and Walters, R.: *Adolescent Aggression,* Ronald Press, New York, 1959.
6. Frank, G.: *The Boston Strangler,* New American Library, New York, 1966.
7. Zusman, J.: *The Social Breakdown Syndrome,* Milbank Memorial Fund, Quarterly, Vol. XVLIV, No. 1, Part 2, 1966.
8. Tinbergen, N.: Science 160 (3835):1411, 1968.
9. Dollard, J., et al: *Frustration and Aggression,* Yale University Press, New Haven, 1939.
10. Sears, R. R., et al: Genet Psychol Monogr, pp. 47 and 135, 1953.
11. Freud, S.: *Collected Papers of Sigmund Freud,* ed. J. Strachey, Vol. 2, Basic Books, New York, 1959.
12. Hartman, H., Kris, E. and Loewenstein, R. M.: *Psychoanalytic Study of the Child,* Vols. 3-4, International Universities Press, New York, 1949.
13. Menninger, K.: *Love Against Hate,* Harcourt, Brace & World, New York, 1942.
14. Fenichel, O.: *The Psychoanalytic Theory of Neurosis,* Norton, New York, 1945.
15. Lorenz, K.: *On Aggression,* Methuen, London, 1966.
16. Eibl-Eibesfeld, I.: *Violence and War, with Clinical Studies,* ed. Masserman, J. H., Gruen and Straton, New York, 1963.
17. Erikson, E. H.: *Identity and the Life Cycle,* International Universities Press, New York, 1959.

EPILOGUE:
Violence, Suicide and Hope

Despite the wide range of research and study that recently has been undertaken on the problem of violence and aggression—as represented by the articles chosen for this collection—it must be clear to the reader by now that there are many unanswered questions. In fact, we face far more questions than we do answers at this stage of study.

Until now, science has hesitated to engage the enormity and complexity of man's violence to his own kind. But it can no longer do so, as our existence is increasingly endangered by our own engines of violence, from automobiles to the nightmarish sophistication of "modern" warfare techniques. If we are to survive, science must face the problem (among others) of human violence —defined both in terms of the individual and of the group, including warfare and civil unrest.

It is fitting to end this book with a discussion of hope, though mention of the word may seem a retreat to sentimentalities and platitudes that avoid the overwhelming reality of the problem. But from the viewpoint of the behavioral sciences, the study of hope can be a very real, constructive approach to the problem. The work of Stotland in *The Psychology of Hope* shows that the attitude of hope can be conceptualized and studied by scientific methods, and that the presence or absence of hope can be a determining force in human behavior.[1]

My interest in hope's relation to violence grew out of curiosity about the similarities between violent and suicidal individuals. Hopelessness is one of those similarities. This, contrasted with the evidence about the positive effects of hope on the results of goal-directed behavior, led to two propositions:

1. Violence, whether in individuals or groups, is essentially self-destructive and tends to occur when hope is lost. The presence of hope is a deterrent to violence.

2. The presence or absence of hope depends on a complex array of factors— but in many cases may be the result of highly subjective perceptions which

may be controlled by conscious effort.

Hope is defined in Stotland's terms as "a shorthand term for an expectation about goal attainment" . . . "The degree of hopefulness is taken as the level of expectation that a given goal can be obtained."

The first proposition can be sufficiently supported by a number of observations. The second proposition is the one that holds the challenge for our efforts —for as little as is known about violence even less is known about the creation, sustenance and effective use of hope as a force.

Clinical observations of individuals who eventually committed suicide show that an attitude of hopelessness can become a delusion which cannot be shaken by reason or psychological intervention. It has even been observed that loss of hope or confidence in a hospital staff can trigger an epidemic of suicides among the patients who are depressed.[2] Other observations show that, contrary to the belief of many, suicidal and violent behavior are not mutually exclusive. Persons attempting suicide often have a history of violent behavior as in studies of the high incidence of suicide among convicted murderers. One study revealed that one-third of the convicted murderers in England between 1950 and 1962 committed suicide.[3] A similar study in the United States of 600 convicted murderers showed a high relative suicide rate of more than 9%.[4] A study of policemen who committed suicide showed that one-third had histories of aggressive, impulsive behavior, and 5.3% had committed murder-suicide.[5] These cases showed a progression of hopelessness that led first to murder, then to suicide; while still other research demonstrates relationships between highly violent behavior in suicide cases and self-destructive tendencies among murderers and other violent individuals.[6]

Hendin, considering the dynamics of an increase in the suicide rate of young blacks in New York City, found a combination of self-hatred and homicidal rage directed toward a racist society as a major dynamic.[7] It was pointed out that the rage of these young blacks was not "unconscious hostility" as often formulated as an underlying factor in suicide, but conscious rage of homicidal intensity pushed beyond the point of control by a combination of personal problems and very real frustrations related to race barriers. This murderous rage is as conscious as that described by Grier and Cobbs in *Black Rage*, an angry, diffuse reaction to the frustrations of unrealized expectations and loss of hope.[8]

According to Stotland, goals maintained as important in the face of hopelessness result in anxiety and possibly violent behavior.[1] If the importance of these goals is denied, anxiety may be avoided in a state of apathy and passive suicide, as among the Jews imprisoned in death camps who gave up hope and lost interest in maintaining even the most basic bodily needs and functions, as observed by Bettelheim and Frankl.[9, 10]

Studies of the condition of life in slum areas continually point to the parallel existence of hopelessness and violence. When social conditions result in feelings of helplessness and self-hatred, violence becomes a way of life.[11] The social challenge which must be met by any comprehensive efforts to lessen violence in our society is clear. If trends toward violence are to be reversed, social conditions which breed hopelessness must be changed.

Does the association between hopelessness and violence appear as a factor under the conditions of organized group behavior? Is group violence inherently self-destructive as is much individual violence? Perhaps the terms "morale" or "esprit de corps" are appropriate when hope is discussed with reference to a group. When a group's morale is high its actions are coordinated and directed toward the successful achievement of its goals. If morale drops, efforts become uncoordinated and incidents of conflicts between individuals or factions within the group increase, resulting in possible failure and dissolution of the group. Moreover, it can be shown that groups become violent when hope is lost.

No more contemporary or important group efforts than the civil rights or black liberation movement could be chosen to consider this question. And in this area particularly the question of violence versus goal-directed behavior inspired by hope is not just an academic consideration but one which may have profound effects on our future as a nation. Hope began to stir among black people with the beginning of the civil rights movement and the achievement of milestones through the U.S. Supreme Court and elsewhere. As equality and true freedom have come to be seen as a possibility, expectations of black people have increased, only to be dashed by a lack of discernible progress among most blacks in education, economic opportunities, and the mutual respect necessary to the breaking down of racist attitudes. Among a people faced with a frustrating lack of progress in economic gains and acceptance as full equals by white American society, while at the same time undergoing a crisis of direction and leadership, impulsive violence occurs with increasing frequency. This had lead to radical black splinter groups espousing "suicidal revolution"—which has taken the form of shoot-outs with police and the inevitable loss of many young, intelligent black leaders.[12] Strong, effective black leadership will be required to unite the black liberation movement and direct it along effective paths if gains are to be won.

Another example of hopelessness underlying violence is the growth of radical left politics among students. This movement, which grew out of new national political consciousness stemming in part from the Vietnam war, seems to have become associated with a depressed, rather hopeless outlook on life among young people. The movement has become increasingly splintered and violent in the past few years dating from the riots during the 1968 Democratic National Convention in Chicago. College youths, bombarded with a new awareness of world problems such as nuclear and biological weaponry, racism, and environmental pollution, plus the dilemma of an unwanted war, have become increasingly involved with these problems and in many instances increasingly hopeless about the future. Much of the sense of hopelessness about the future and rejection of the status quo may be based on a projection of feelings of a lack of confidence in achieving goals. The many shortcomings of society provide the ideal focus for a group of young people totally devoid of confidence in their ability to achieve their goals, and an increase in violent acts by some of the young radicals has been the result.

In listening to the most radical and violent of these we hear a total disillusionment with the present system even as a basis for change, as evidenced in an interview with a youthful "bomber" that recently appeared in Life magazine: "We are revolutionaries, not reformists. We are not trying to frighten the establishment, we are trying to destroy it so that a just society can be built on human values . . . The children in this society . . . have had their eyes opened to the nature of this society and refuse to be a part of it. At some point in the future it might be politically correct to attack also the heads of major war industries . . . It's not important whether I personally see the successful conclusion of the first real American revolution. It is only necessary to be a part of it. *I haven't been depressed since I realized I was part of the revolutionary process.*"[13]

Below the surface rhetoric of political idealism and radicalism is heard a sense of hopelessness in the future. These young people do not seem to be proceeding toward any specified utopian dreams or goals but rather projecting their hopelessness and translating it into a feeling of the need to destroy the present system with unflinching acceptance of any violence necessary to do so. Often suicidal violence and destruction, as expressions of the attitude of hopelessness, have become ends in themselves, creating a sense of purpose as well as the basis for emotional catharsis. The violent outbursts may be seen as a last ditch defense against feelings of despair, a transition from despair and depression into a more positive state gained through identification with a "cause."

Because of the close relationship between hopelessness and violence, the establishment and maintenance of hope has the potential of being a powerful deterrent to violence in many instances. The challenge lies in the problem of effectively creating hope based on the realities of any given situation. The presence or absence of an attitude of hope in an individual will depend on a number of possible variables, including the presence of various types of depressive illness, the development of a lack of hope and trust due to early emotional deprivation, a low tolerance for frustration, possible organic factors, and most important, powerful reinforcements delivered by socio-economic conditions affecting the individual.

The impact of environmental deprivation on an individual must be considered a major factor to be overcome in attempting to increase levels of hope among minority and lower socio-economic groups. Chronic failure and deprivation generating hopelessness takes its toll on individuals leading to apathy and chronic lack of confidence which will not easily be dispelled by an increase in educational and economic opportunities alone."[11] Programs resulting solely from great infusions of money may be relatively ineffective if the problem of motivating chronically hopeless individuals is not first solved.

What are the techniques for the creation of hope among groups and individuals? In *The Psychology of Hope*, Stotland observes that hope can be preserved in the face of great, difficult goals by setting partial goals which can be obtained one at a time over a long period. This technique transfers hope directed toward the total goal to each partial goal. The acquisition of each partial goal adds to confidence in the attainment of the major goal of the group, and helps maintain hope over the long struggle.[1]

More must be learned and disseminated concerning the qualities of successful leaders, especially with regard to their appreciation of hope as a creative force. Responsible and successful leaders are needed to manage the tremendous power of group hope so that a maximum of change can be brought about with a minimum of violence. The emergence of a black leader —to replace the slain Rev. Martin Luther King Jr.—with the charisma to mobilize sufficient political power to unite the various factions of blacks would give rise to hope which could hasten the achievement of major goals. Destructive leaders who are depressed and mobilize support through appeals to hopelessness should be recognized not only as likely failures in achieving group goals but as promoters of useless violence.

Another social medium for the cure of hopelessness might be developed through the prison system, changing it from a cradle of violence into a positive social agency. Sufficient investment in developing methods for rehabilitating criminal offenders might mean a great saving to society in the long run in terms of the cost of criminal acts and violence. Perhaps new demonstration projects of training and job placement centers run with psychological sophistication could supplement the developments in prisons with an emphasis on rehabilitation.

We need more examples of the possibility of creative solutions to the needs of youth to improve the human features of any given system. Many creative outlets for this critical but restless energy could be devised, especially with models such as Ralph Nader, who has been able to force large corporations to comply with higher safety standards through public exposure and pressure.[14] Nader's aggressive efforts toward safety in automobiles, although not as sensational or dramatic as violent confrontations, have undoubtedly saved more lives than any demonstrations of defiance against corporations or other groups by radical youths. A more recent movement, John Gardner's "Common Cause," is attempting to organize around efforts to inform people of upcoming governmental decisions with arguments for and against. This organization focuses public opinion on various segments of government as well as individuals in attempting to form a "people's lobby" to express the common will. Groups organized to apply economic pressure toward constructive causes through realistic, attainable goals, such as well-led minority groups, unions, and other interest groups, can *avoid violence* through the *aggressive* pursuit of reasonable goals, generating hope for the attainment of important long-range causes and goals.

Whenever individuals band together in a group, there is bound to be some form of competition for needs and wants of those individuals and groups with the inherent potential for violence, depending on many conditions. No utopian society can abolish this competition. However, a wider understanding of the methods by which hope of attaining various goals is increased, as well as the actual probability of success toward these goals, would lessen the prevalence of violent behavior. No utopian world free of all violence is possible as long as humans inhabit the planet, but reducing violence by organizing people around attainable goals to maximize hope is indeed possible. Sustained and systematic attention to the core dynamics of violence such as hope might reverse the trends toward violence increasingly evident in modern society, and even save us from any kind of awesome mass suicide.

REFERENCES

1. Stotland, E.: *The Psychology of Hope.* Jossey-Bass, Inc., San Francisco, 1969.
2. Kobler, A. L. and Stotland, E.: *The End of Hope.* The Free Press of Glencoe: Collier MacMillian Limited, London, 1964.
3. Gibson, E. and Klein, S.: *Murder.* H. M. Stationery Office, London, 1961.
4. Dublin, L. I. and Bunzel, B.: Survey Graphic 24:127-131, 1935.
5. Friedman, P.: In *Essays in Self Destruction.* Ed. by E. Shneidman. Science House, Inc., New York, 1967.
6. West, D. J.: *Murder Followed by Suicide.* Harvard University Press, Cambridge, 1966.
7. Hendin, H.: Archives of General Psychiatry 21:407, 1969.
8. Grier, W. H. and Cobbs, P. M.: *Black Rage.* Basic Books, Inc., New York, 1968.
9. Bettelheim, B.: Journal Abnormal and Social Psychology 38:417-452, 1943.
10. Frankl, V.: *From Death-Camp to Existentialism.* Beacon Press-Beacon Hill, Boston, 1959 (Part I, pp. 1-93).
11. Harrington, M.: *The Other America.* Penguin Books, Baltimore, 1962.
12. Le Blanc, P.: Chicago Tribune Sunday Magazine, p. 114, December 6, 1970.
13. Life Magazine, p. 24, March 27, 1970.
14. Wall Street Journal, p. 32, November 19, 1970.